Bill 'Swampy' Marsh is an award-winning writer/performer of stories, songs and plays. He spent most of his youth in rural south-western New South Wales. Bill was forced to give up any idea he had of a 'career' as a cricketer when a stint at agricultural college was curtailed due to illness, and so began his hobby of writing. After backpacking through three continents and working in the wine industry, his writing hobby blossomed into a career.

His first collection of short stories, *Beckom Pop. 64*, was published in 1988, his second, *Old Yanconian Daze*, in 1995 and his third, *Looking for Dad*, in 1998. During 1999, Bill released *Australia*, a CD of his songs and stories. That was followed in 2002 by *A Drover's Wife* and *Glory, Glory: A Tribute to the Royal Flying Doctor Service* in 2008 and *Open Roads: The Songs and Stories of Bill Swampy Marsh* in 2017. He has written soundtrack songs and music for the television documentaries *The Last Mail from Birdsville: The Story of Tom Kruse*; *Source to Sea: The Story of the Murray Riverboats* and the German travel documentaries *Traumzeit auf dem Stuart Highway*, *Clinic Flights (Tilpa & Marble Bar)*, *Traumzeit in den Kimberleys* and *Einsatz von Port Hedland nach Marble Bar*.

Bill has won and judged many nationwide short-story and songwriting competitions and short-film awards as well as running writing workshops throughout Australia. He has performed his songs and stories from outback places such as Mount Dare (pop. 10), down the Birdsville Track, as part of the

Great Australian Cattle Drive; on the Ghan as part of Great Southern Rail's ANZAC Tribute Journey; and at the Transport Hall of Fame gala dinner in Alice Springs as a support act to Slim Dusty.

Great Australian Outback Yarns draws from Bill's very successful series of 'Great Australian' stories, which includes: *Great Australian Volunteer Firies Stories* (2021), *Great Australian Outback Trucking Stories* (2019), *Great Australian Bush Funeral Stories* and *Great Australian Bush Priests Stories* (2018), *Great Australian Outback Nurses Stories* (2017), *Great Australian Outback Teaching Stories* (2016), *Great Australian Outback Police Stories* (2015), *Amazing Grace: Stories of Faith and Friendship from Outback Australia* (2014), *The Complete Book of Australian Flying Doctor Stories* and *Great Australian Outback School Stories* (2013), *Great Australian CWA Stories* (2011), *New Great Australian Flying Doctor Stories* and *The ABC Book of Great Aussie Stories for Young People* (2010), *Great Australian Stories: Outback Towns and Pubs* (2009), *More Great Australian Flying Doctor Stories* (2007), *Great Australian Railway Stories* (2005), *Great Australian Droving Stories* (2003), *Great Australian Shearing Stories* (2001) and *Great Australian Flying Doctor Stories* (1999). Bill's biography *Goldie: Adventures in a Vanishing Australia* was published in 2008 and his semi-autobiographical collection *Swampy: Tall Tales and True from Boyhood and Beyond* was published in 2012.

More information about the author can be found at
www.billswampymarsh.com
Facebook: Bill 'Swampy' Marsh

GREAT AUSTRALIAN OUTBACK YARNS: VOLUME 1

BILL 'SWAMPY' MARSH

ABC
BOOKS

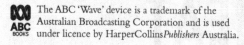 The ABC 'Wave' device is a trademark of the Australian Broadcasting Corporation and is used under licence by HarperCollins*Publishers* Australia.

HarperCollins*Publishers*
Australia • Brazil • Canada • France • Germany • Holland • Hungary
India • Italy • Japan • Mexico • New Zealand • Poland • Spain • Sweden
Switzerland • United Kingdom • United States of America

First published in Australia in 2021
by HarperCollinsPublishers Australia Pty Limited
Level 13, 201 Elizabeth Street, Sydney NSW 2000
ABN 36 009 913 517
harpercollins.com.au

This is a combined volume of stories drawn from fourteen of Bill Marsh's previous books: *Great Australian Flying Doctor Stories* (1999), *Great Australian Shearing Stories* (2001), *Great Australian Railway Stories* (2005), *More Great Australian Flying Doctor Stories* (2007), *Great Australian Stories: Outback Towns and Pubs* (2009), *New Great Australian Flying Doctor Stories* (2010), *Great Australian CWA Stories* (2011), *Great Australian Outback School Stories* (2013), *Great Australian Outback Police Stories* (2015), *Great Australian Outback Teaching Stories* (2016), *Great Australian Outback Nurses Stories* (2017), *Great Australian Bush Funeral Stories* (2018), *Great Australian Bush Priests Stories* (2018), *Great Australian Trucking Stories* (2019).

Copyright © Bill Marsh 1999, 2001, 2005, 2007, 2009, 2010, 2011, 2015, 2016, 2017, 2018, 2019, 2021

The right of Bill Marsh to be identified as the author of this work has been asserted by him in accordance with the *Copyright Amendment (Moral Rights) Act 2000*.

A catalogue record for this book is available from the National Library of Australia.

ISBN 978 0 7333 4215 8 (paperback)
ISBN 978 1 4607 1439 3 (ebook)

Cover design by Darren Holt, HarperCollins Design Studio
Cover image: Stuart Arms Hotel bar, 1921, Alice Springs, Northern Territory, by Jack Laver, courtesy State Library of South Australia [PRG 1365/1/445]
Typeset in ITC Bookman Light by HarperCollins Design Studio
Printed and bound in Australia by McPherson's Printing Group

From Bill 'Swampy' Marsh,
May the stories within bring you
a smile and brighten up your day.

Contents

Beckom, NSW

(Outback Towns and Pubs)

As a young kid I lived in a small town in the south-west of New South Wales called Beckom. Back then, Beckom only had a population of sixty-four. I know the exact number because whenever I had difficulty sleeping, instead of counting sheep, I'd systematically count the people in town. Of course, with so few of us, we didn't have a library and so books were hard to access. Instead, people told their stories. Some were true to life. Some were much larger than life. Still, tragic or humorous, tall or tender, it became the craft of the storyteller to try and make their tales as entertaining as possible. And that's how I grew up: sitting on the front step of the Beckom pub, waiting for Dad, and listening intently to those old masters, the likes of Bob O'Riley, Frank Langley, Terry Golden, Errol Foster and so forth, spin their yarns. So, I guess, my craft had its roots away back then. It's been my passion ever since, and I'm still learning.

To pick the moment when I came to realise this is hard to pinpoint. But, in a funny sort of way, I'd say it all began during a cold winter in about the late 1950s. Our school teacher was a man called Mr Donovan and so when Mum found out that amongst his wife's many fine qualities lurked a certified piano teacher, my fate was sealed. Week after week through black, frosted mornings I crunched my way to piano lessons — ears and fingers bitten from the savage cold — fumbling painfully for forgotten notes. Then, halfway through Lesson 10 of Practical Piano Grade 1, I was ordered to pull up my socks if I was going to play 'God Save the Queen' at the start of the town concert.

This was news to me.

Apparently a variety night was being organised to raise money to renovate Beckom's leaning corrugated-iron War Memorial Hall. All acts were invited to perform and one of Goodtime Charlie's singing mates, from his old 'Wild West' days, had agreed to be the star attraction. The star's name was Rocky Rivers. Rumour had it that someone had even heard him singing over the wireless on a Saturday Night Country and Western Show. So it was to be a big occasion. So big, in fact, that even our publican, Bluey Saunders, had agreed to close the pub for the night and set up a bar in the hall to ensure maximum attendance. Mrs Donovan was to be the MC as well as play a classical piano piece, sing an opera song and organise the yet non-existent school choir.

There were fifteen of us kids attending Beckom Public School, ranging from five to fourteen years old, all of us having been weathered by life's elements, even at our tender ages: washed by flood and rain, burnt by sun and bushfire, dried to the core by drought, frozen by frost, pitted in skin by dust and hail. But not a single one amongst us knew the first thing about the gentle art of song. Then, to make matters worse, Brownie, McCaughney and me bowed under pressure and agreed to perform the popular hit song of the day — 'Donald, Where's Yer Trousers'.

Six weeks isn't a long time when even the basics have to be learned. The whole town suffered under a cloud of rehearsal fatigue. Sheep sales took a dive. The football team started its run of losses. Even the pub became a more contemplative place as men sipped on their schooners, their minds locked in silent rehearsal.

But above it all soared Mrs Donovan. She pranced and gesticulated, shouting advice and encouragement through her clattering false teeth at our retrogressive school choir. She galvanised the women of the area and had soon organised the printing and distribution of the advertising posters. She organised the cleaning, washing and decoration of the hall. She organised the mending and arrangement of the seating. She helped cook supper for the big night. Almost single-handedly she built the whole town up to fever pitch.

A certain quiet washed Beckom on the day of the concert. What wasn't learned by now would never be learned. All us 'entertainers' were in the hands of the unknown, treading on virgin ground. Butterflies fluttered within our stomachs, breeding rapidly as the day gathered pace. By tea time any desire for food had been replaced by a deep hollow feeling of tense sickness.

News spread that Rocky Rivers had arrived in town and was renewing his friendship with Goodtime Charlie over in the pub. Adults and school kids alike drifted in the vicinity, hoping to catch a glimpse of that star whose voice had floated over the airwaves. There was laughter from within the pub but no one dared enter, for we knew now, from personal experience, just how temperamental some entertainers could get before a big performance.

I stepped out onto the stage, mortified with panic, and sat at the piano. The hall was packed to the hilt with over sixty expectant people. The eyes of the world seemed upon me. Mrs Donovan stepped into the footlights and hushed the throng. 'I ask you all to be upstanding for "God Save the Queen". To lead you on piano we have Bill "Swampy" Marsh.'

I somehow managed the opening chord, then my fingers refused to move. They dangled over the piano as strung skeletons, mesmerised by the daunting task before them — ten complete strangers to my body. Mrs Donovan began singing. The audience followed suit. Then, mid-anthem, my fingers inexplicably reared and began to first trot, then to canter over the keyboard. Two-thirds through I'd caught up with the cacophony of voices surrounding me. But, by now, my momentum was such that I galloped past them as if they were standing still, leaving them in my dust. I'd finished playing, stood up, and was heading off stage even before the audience had entered the last line.

'And now the school choir to enchant you with "Greensleeves".

I felt safer in a crowd of my own kind. United against a common foe — the audience — we stumbled on stage to take up our appointed positions. Mrs Donovan signalled our start and we carried the song off, sounding more like a lost flock of Border Leicesters than an enchanting choral group.

But we survived.

'And to complete the school's performance for tonight we have the "Three Likely Lads" with their rendition of "Donald, Where's Your Trousers".'

The instant we walked out on stage we knew it was a mistake. Dressed in mock kilts that'd been shaped from older sisters' skirts, and with sporrans semi-fashioned from recently caught rabbits' pelts, the wolf whistles and crude remarks echoed the tin hall. Brownie wet himself. McCaughney opened his mouth but not a word came out. So it was left to me, the veteran of 'God Save the Queen' and 'Greensleeves', and I fled through the song like a chipmunk on fire before diving for the security of back stage, leaving my mates, wet and wordless, to sort out their own fates.

It was then Mum's turn to grace the footlights. Mum'd dreamed of being a great performer all her life; reading all the entertainment magazines and singing along with the tunes on the wireless. But, unfortunately, the transition from kitchen to stage proved too difficult a hurdle for that lady of dreams, upon that icy winter's night, and she fainted in front of a packed house.

Things started to improve after Mum was aided off stage, as each performer learned the necessary survival skills from the previous act's mistakes. Porky Squealer gave us a grand performance of pig impersonations. From Landrace sow through to Wessex Saddleback boar he had their 'oinking' sounds down to perfection. Big Red Brewster stepped up and gave an unbelievable darts display whereupon, landing his first dart in the bullseye, his second and third darts lodged themselves tight beside the first. And all from a distance of five paces.

At Doctor Granger's command, Buster, the town's adopted dog, twice entered the audience to return on stage carrying a shoe between his teeth. The third time into the hall, Buster returned with a pair of lady's knickers. This brought the house down and sent eyes darting in all directions in search of the owner. Bluey Saunders took time off from behind the bar to give a rousing rendition of 'The Man from Beckom'. He'd changed the town's name from 'Ironbark' which did nothing for the rhyming of the poem but the sentiment remained.

Following Bluey came Mrs Donovan. She broached the piano like she was stalking a stray wether. She sat, raised her hands ready for attack, then crashed, banged and walloped her way through a frenzied piano piece written by a German named Beethoven. She followed that up with a song from an Italian opera. No one understood the words but, still, she was given a standing ovation and we suffered through the encore, knowing that this night wouldn't have happened but for her efforts. She deserved all our applause, and more.

Mrs McCaughney then appeared, unannounced, to perform a version of the 'Dance of the Seven Veils'. As the women muttered their misgivings, the cheering and foot-stamping from around the bar raised such a dust storm that I remained only to dream of the nakedness I imagined behind those light, floating, coloured veils.

Amid this scene of careless profusion was helped the star of the show, Rocky Rivers. Dad propped the beer-sodden body upon a stool, guitar limply hanging in hand. Empty stool to his side. As we looked towards that derelict man — this star of wireless — our whole world stopped spinning. He lifted his head as if by winch, gazed at us as though we were miles away, somewhere over near Ariah Park. His bloodshot eyes rolled in their sockets. As we waited for his first utterance you could've heard a feather drop. We sat, frightened, quivering at this drunken star's mercy.

'Wheeeeersh ssme ol' mate ssCharlie?'

Dad rushed out the back to get Goodtime Charlie out of the dunny while Rocky Rivers struggled to get some focus on his audience. We, in turn, sat before him, mouths agape. Seconds passed like minutes until Dad and Bluey returned with Goodtime Charlie and helped him onto the vacant stool on stage. Rocky Rivers placed a loving arm around his mate and announced, 'Shemeee 'n' Charl' wou' like ter ssshing yer some sssshongs.'

Then he lifted his guitar. Started a slow strum. His mouth opened and out fell a pure velvet voice ... 'There's a bridle hanging on the wall ...'

Goodtime Charlie, as if called to heel by his mate's voice, raised his head. His ears pricked. His eyes began to sparkle. Then he smiled and he joined in as if singing a diamond hymn. Apprehension washed from our hearts. They sang songs of horses, which brought the smell of sweated flanks to the nostrils. Songs of flood and drought. Songs torn out of blistered and bloodied hands. Songs of the raw earth being cracked by disc-ploughs. Songs that'd erupted from deep within working-men's souls. They sang songs of love that made the men look down at their riding boots and the women fumble for their handkerchiefs.

To this glorious sound, my leaden eyes fell into slumber. I was lifted, carried, and placed onto the back seat of our chilly car. Tightly wrapped in a blanket, I dreamed I was a singer, a storyteller, travelling the country; bringing hope to the despairing, laughter to the sad, love to the lonely. Then I dreamed that I had to play 'God Save the Queen' before every performance.

The Train

(Railway Stories)

I don't know exactly how old I was when this happened, but it was at primary school. I recall our teacher standing in front of our class of five kids and announcing the news that, 'Throughout the history of the modern world, the train has played an important part as a purveyor of free trade'. And that's when Brownie, McCaughney and me came up with the idea.

See, we'd noticed that by the time the South West Mail reached our remote little settlement of Beckom, Pop. 64, the passengers were slumped into a deep, sedentary mental state and it was while they were in this vulnerable condition that we felt they'd more than likely be prepared to buy anything. This, we hoped, included our abundance of figs.

Just once a week that old passenger train huffed, puffed, clattered and rocked its way slowly into Beckom railway station, there to rest its tired parts for a while and take on much-needed water and coal. So it was during this respite that Brownie, McCaughney and me decided to open up trade links with the outside world. We calculated that from the first sight of smoke on the horizon to the South West Mail's arrival at the station took about twenty to thirty minutes, depending upon the wind. And that'd give us enough time to pick a few buckets of figs and set up our little stall opposite where the passenger carriages stopped. We even painted a sign to announce our intentions. It read:

FRESH FIGS
1 PENNY A DOZEN

Now, old Tom, the widowed stationmaster, was all for it. He reckoned that our enterprise would not only help brighten up his week but our noisy arrival would also remind him that it was train day, an occasion he was apt to forget from time to time.

Anyhow, that first week of trade, all the figs sold immediately. You could see the keenness in the eyes of those weary travellers as they willingly exchanged their money for our produce. So relieved were these people from distant parts to look at a different human face for their brief time of stopover that, even after all the figs had been sold, they still crowded around us. They touched us to see if we were real and they tried to engage us in deep conversation by asking us questions like, 'What are your names?' and 'What class are you in at school?' Some even questioned us as to, 'What the bloody hell do you do for entertainment in a place like this?'

By the next week, when that old steam train had ground to a halt in our carefully set trade trap, we'd boosted the price of the figs up to threepence per dozen. And even though there were a few muffled complaints about both the price and the quality of our produce, the lot again sold effortlessly.

Fig season soon came to its mushy end but in its place came oranges and almost-fresh ginger beer. Again, all stocks were snapped up eagerly, even at hugely inflated prices.

They say that success breeds success. And that's true because before long I was giving a well-received, and paid for, rendition of 'You Are My Sunshine' with old Tom playing the gum leaf, while Brownie wrestled with three tennis balls in an act he described as 'juggling'. Then McCaughney's broken leg proved to be such a great attraction that long after it'd mended he still wore the plaster cast. Oh, how those poor, travel-bored souls almost tripped over themselves just to pay for the privilege of signing their names on that dirty, scrappy, bit of plaster. And McCaughney's rendition of how the accident occurred was told so differently and graphically to each train load of people that, before long, we'd all forgotten how the leg was originally broken.

But the money kept pouring in.

Then one week the strangest thing happened. It was a still day and no smoke appeared on the horizon. Brownie jumped off the platform, put his ear to the railway track and reported that a train was definitely on its way. This we found hard to believe so we hopped down to join him and, yes, sure enough, an approaching train could be heard along the rails.

Then, echoing in the distance, there came a whistle. But somehow this whistle sounded different from the one we were used to hearing. This was more a sound of warning than of welcome. Together, we all stood at the platform's edge, gawking out along the track. Then, from out of the shimmering mirage appeared a monster the like of which we'd never seen before. We scampered back behind our small stall and huddled there for safety as this metal monstrosity roared down upon us with all the fury of a wild storm. It completely ignored Beckom and thundered by as if we never even existed. It left us quaking in our shorts and sandals.

In search of answers we looked at old Tom. 'Oh, that's one of them new diesel locomotives,' he said. 'They don't need no water or coal so there's no reason for 'em to stop in a small little town like this.' And I'm sure that I saw the tears welling in his eyes.

Turning back we witnessed the captured train carriages being dragged off, rudely, into the distance by this new diesel locomotive. Then we packed up our unsold produce and we walked home in stunned silence, amazed at just how viciously technology had severed our trading ties with the outside world.

The Haunted Cemetery

(Bush Funeral Stories)

It was quite common knowledge around town that our cemetery had a haunted ghost. Everybody knew about it and so nobody ever went into the cemetery at night for fear of what might happen to them. Anyway, there were these two old codgers. They lived next to one another in a street that was just the other side of the cemetery. Now, for years and years, every night of the week these two old codgers would meet up and they'd walk down the street, turn right at the southern end, then follow along another street that bordered the cemetery, to go on to the pub. Every night they done that, without fail.

So this night they're in the pub. It's the middle of winter. The weather's terrible; it's cold and rainy and windy, lightning and thunder, the lot. Like I said, it was a real horrible night. Anyhow, it might've been one of their birthdays or something because they'd really got stuck into it and they'd had quite a few more than they usually did, which would've been a hell of a lot to start with. Anyway, it's getting late. It's near closing time and the first old codger says to the second old bloke, 'I'm done,' he says, 'I'm heading off home. See yer tomorra'.'

'Okay,' says the second feller. 'I won't be long. I'll just have anotherie 'n head off home meself.'

'See yer,' says the first feller.

'Not if I see yer first,' says the second feller; you know, as a sort of joke.

So the first old feller gets outside. Like I said it's a horrible, miserable winter's night; rain, hail, wind, the lot. It's as black as all black can get — that's apart from the flashes of lightning that electrify up the sky. Anyhow, he starts to stagger off home. Down the street that borders the cemetery he goes. The wind's lashing at him, rain and hail are biting at his face. 'Bugger it,' he says. 'Not even a haunted ghost would come out on a night like this, so I'll take a short cut through the cemetery.'

The thing is, there's a funeral on tomorrow and they've already dug the grave. So this feller's staggering through the cemetery. Next thing, down the hole he goes, straight to the bottom. *Plop.* So now he starts grappling at the muddy bank of the grave, trying to get out. But the sides are so slippery that he can't get a grip, and before long he's all worn out. 'Bugger it,' he says, 'I've had enough. I may as well camp here in the back corner of the grave for the rest of the night 'n someone'll get me out in the morning.' So that's what he does. He settles down for the night at the back end of the grave.

By now it's closing time at the pub and so his mate's heading home. Same as before; the wind's lashing him, rain and hail are biting at his face. 'Bugger it,' he says, 'a haunted ghost wouldn't come out on a night like this so I'll take a short cut through the cemetery.'

So this second feller starts staggering through the cemetery. Next thing, down the same hole he goes, straight to the muddy bottom. *Splat.* And now he also starts scrabbling, ripping at the side of the grave, trying to get a foothold, in an attempt to get out. And as he's trying and trying, slipping and sliding, falling down and getting back up again, a voice comes from the back of the grave, 'You'll never get out of here, mate.'

Next thing — *zoom* — he takes off like a rocket shot out of Cape Canaveral. Straight up and out of that six-feet-deep hole he shoots, and he's gone into the night. When he got home he locked all his doors and windows and he scrambled under his bed. And that's where he stayed. No one saw him for a week.

Cato, NSW

(Outback Towns and Pubs)

Because my parents split up when I was young I was brought up by my grandparents. So I can only ever remember living with my grandfather and grandmother. But I never lacked for love or loving care or anything, and I just adored my grandfather. Grandfather's name was Charlie. He wasn't that tall but he was very stocky and, from my earliest time, I remember how, whenever any of his old mates from the bush or some relatives came down, they'd pat me on the head and say, 'You know, Fred, your grandfather's one of the greatest grass-fighters the back country's ever seen?'

Grass-fighting's different to in-the-ring-fighting in as much as, with in-the-ring-fighting, you wear boxing gloves. Grass-fighting's the bare-knuckled fighting that happens out the back of dance halls or out the back of pubs. It's the real fair-dinkum stuff. So it made me wonder how such a kind and gentle man, as Grandfather was, could even get involved in something like that. So much so that, in those very early days, I even thought that by 'grass-fighting' they meant that he'd lie down and punch hell out of the lawn or he'd roll around with a clump of saltbush or whatever because I just could not imagine him out the back of a pub having a bare-fist fight.

Anyway, I always wanted to work on the Broken Hill mine, with Grandfather. That never quite happened because he retired before I got a job there. Then, when I did, Grandfather always used to offer to drive me to work. And it didn't take long for me to find out that his kind offer was made because, if he did, then he also had to come and pick me up and, on the way home we'd just happen to pass a pub and he'd say, 'Do yer feel like a beer?'

'Yeah, I feel like a beer.'

And so we'd go into the pub. And, when we did, we'd always just happen to run into a few of Grandfather's grey-haired old mates or some old codgers that'd known him from somewhere and it was always a warm, 'G'day, Charlie. Want a drink?' Then, inevitably, at one stage or other, they'd say to me, 'Yer know, yer grandfather's one'a the greatest grass-fighters the outback's ever seen? Oh, yer just should'a seen 'im.'

So then, when we'd get home and we were having tea, I'd say, 'What's this about you being a great grass-fighter, Grandfather?'

And he'd say, 'Oh, it's nothing', and he'd leave it at that.

Anyway, this particular time, after work, Grandfather and I were in the pub and an old mate he hadn't seen for years come in for a drink and they were talking and going on and when Grandfather's mate was about to leave I said, 'Goodbye,' and this old green-eye said, 'Yer know yer grandfather's one'a the greatest grass-fighters the west's ever seen?'

I would've been about twenty-two or twenty-three by this stage and Grandfather would've been in his late sixties, say. So that night we were having tea and I insisted that I get the story. 'Come on,' I said, 'what's all this about you being a great grass-fighter?'

'It's nothing,' he said, and he just left it at that.

Anyhow, Grandmother's eyes used to twinkle when she was in a humorous mood and she said, 'Oh, go on, Charlie, tell him.'

And this's the story as I got it.

Apparently they were reasonably newly married. Grandmother was pregnant with my father and they took over the proprietorship of this hotel at Cato. Cato was up on a tributary of the Darling River system, out from Bourke somewhere. I saw it on an old map once, though I don't think the place exists anymore. But it was on a ford, which was where the bullock wagons and the stage coaches and that crossed the river. So, of course, all the old bullockers would stop there and the stage coach passengers used to stop there and all the shearers and itinerants would stop there on their way through. It was a real meeting point. Whenever anyone was going through that back country they had to go past Cato.

Anyway, so Grandfather's there with a pregnant wife and, as what happened in those days, whenever possible, pregnant ladies always had a female companion. So out from Sydney came Grandfather's sister, Alice. Alice was about seventeen at that time. Gorgeous looking too, as you can see in some of them old photos over there. So Alice came out to Cato to become Grandmother's companion. But, in doing so, she'd left her boyfriend behind in Sydney. They were later to marry. Fred Kerr was his name and, even by then, Fred and Grandfather were the greatest of mates; always ready to try and put one over, whenever an opportunity arose.

Now Fred had been a real Sydney street-kid. He'd learned to stick up for himself by the time he was five. He worked on the wharves and if there was anything he liked, it was a fight. Oh, he loved to fight. But the thing was, apart from the love of a good stoush, even though he was pretty much self-educated, he'd also developed a great love of the English language. He used to roll these beautiful and eloquent words around his tongue. He was like a gardener with a beautiful rose. He just had to use all this wonderful, flowery language and, what's more, he dressed to suit. To use the common word of the day, as tough as he was with his fists, he dressed like a true English 'dandy'. A back country shearer or a bullocker might come up with a more derogatory term, but we'll get to that.

But the story is, when Alice came out to be a companion to Grandmother, Fred missed her terribly. So he decides to come out to Cato. He arrives. He gets off the stage coach. And there he is, 'the essence of sartorial elegance', as he would put it, with his white boater hat, black and white striped blazer, a cravat with a pin through it, sparkling white-cream trousers, spats, shoes, and a little baton, with a jewel embedded in the end of it. Now, you might be able to imagine what sort of impression this made on the local clientele of bullockies, hard-bitten shearers, outback ruffians and the like. Anyhow, he gets off the stage coach and he walks into this rowdy bar. He raps his baton on the bar. Grandfather comes up. Fred gives him a bit of a wink and he announces in a loud voice, 'A modicum of your famous ale, please, publican.'

Grandfather goes and gets Fred a beer. He comes back. Fred says, 'Thank you, my fine gentleman,' and he takes a delicate and savoury sip.

As I said, the place is full of just about every sort of ruffian the back country could produce. Of course, they're all quite bemused by all this carry-on and so one of the roustabouts — a huge feller, he was, in a dirty blue singlet — he comes up and he starts feeling the material of Fred's blazer. 'Not bad stuff, mate,' he says, and he looks around to his mates who are smirking at the show. Then the rousie went one further and he tried to pull the pin out of Fred's cravat.

'Unhand me, sire,' says Fred, 'or I shall remonstrate with thee most severely.'

But, egged on by his mates, this bloke persisted. So Fred says, 'Desist at once, sire, or I shall be forced to handle you, physically.'

'Will yer,' says the roustabout.

'Yes I shall,' replies Fred.

The rousie says, 'So how's about we go outside 'n' settle it, then.'

So they go out the back of the pub to have this grass-fight. Everyone follows, even Grandfather. Then Grandfather described Fred taking off his boater; just like this — very showy — and he very carefully placed it on an old gum tree stump. Then he pulled off his gloves, fingers, one by one, neatly, and puts them down there, beside his boater. Takes off his blazer, folds it two or three times, and just puts it down there. Brushes a speck of dust off it. Rolls up his sleeves. 'Now, sire, are you ready for your lesson in the fine art of pugilism?', which brings smatterings of laughter all around.

Of course, this roustabout's half-full of beer and so he's pretty steamed up by now and so, when Fred finally shapes up, the bloke comes charging in at him, throwing hay-makers left, right and centre. Of course, Fred being a seasoned street fighter neatly ducks aside and 'bang', with a straight right, into the rousie's belly button, which takes the wind out of him, and then 'thwack', one to the jaw, to straighten him up, followed by two or three sharp jabs into the ribs for good measure and down goes this huge roustabout, like the proverbial sack of potatoes. He's out to it.

Well this feller's mates didn't like the outcome of that. It's, 'Hey, yer can't get away with that, yer bloody city slicker.' So in comes one of the rousie's mates and Fred goes 'bang!', straight into the mush and down the second feller goes; out cold. Then in comes another feller, 'bang!', the same thing. Followed by another feller, 'bang!'. And before long there's about ten or fifteen of them, all lying out cold, and Fred hasn't even got a scratch on him. So then all these outback ruffians decided that discretion's the better part of valour and so they all tumble back into the pub and they all want to buy Fred a drink. He's their hero now. He's their new best mate. 'We'll shout yer a drink,' they're all saying.

Then someone called out, 'Hey, mate, where did yer learn ter fight like that?'

And Fred pointed his baton at Grandfather and he said, 'That gentleman there, behind the bar, Charlie, he taught me everything I know about the art of pugilism.' And everybody looked over at Grandfather in awe. 'Yes,' Fred added, 'so don't ever pick on him.' Then he pushed back the hair on his forehead and he said, 'See that scar there.' Actually, he'd fallen down a hold in a ship somewhere and he'd had about eight stitches.

Everyone looked. 'Yeah,' they said.

Fred said, 'Charlie gave me that one when I forgot to duck one of his left hooks.' And he had another bit of a scar on his stomach and so he opened up his spotless shirt and he said, 'See that one there. That's where Charlie busted four of my ribs.'

And there was a stunned silence in the bar and Grandmother said, 'And, after that, if anyone was a bit noisy in the Cato pub, Grandfather would just bang the bar, with his hand, and say, "Righto, fellers, that's enough."'

And it was, 'Yes Charlie.' 'Alright Charlie.' 'Sorry about that Charlie.'

And that's how Grandfather became known as the best grass-fighter in the back country.

The War Hero

(Railway Stories)

I remember when I was about five — it was near the end of the war, like — coming into the kitchen and finding me mum bawling her eyes out. Now, I was wondering what the bloody hell was going on when I saw a letter, written by me dad, sitting there on the table, and I can remember it to this day. It read:

> *Dear Doris,*
> *I have got the VD and am in Lae hospital and will be sent*
> *home as soon as I am well enough to travel ...*

Well, you could've guessed how I felt. I mean, how many kids do you know who can proudly stand up and say that their dad's got the VD? And I imagined how he got it too: swinging from tree to tree, machine gun blazing, chucking hand grenades and rounding up half the Jap army in an afternoon. And there was me mum, crying with relief that Dad was still alive. So I starts off down the street shouting the good news to all the kids, 'Me dad's got the VD! Me dad's got the VD!'

Well, bugger me dead, if like in a flash Mum wasn't out of that house, grabs me in three strides, and drags me back in to the kitchen and, boy, didn't she give me a good dressing-down.

'Now, Swampy, I want you to promise me on the Bible that you won't tell a living soul about yer father gettin' the VD.'

Then Mum tells me that there's spies in the town and if they found out about Dad, they'd kill him when he got home. So I promised not to tell ... and I made the few friends I told promise not to tell either. But I had the feeling that somehow the news spread a bit anyway, because people began dropping around home all concerned about me dad's unfortunate state of health.

Well, soon it was close to the day of me dad's return and, to my amazement, Mum wasn't going to too much trouble over the big event, and the town wasn't preparing anything either. Great thanks, eh, to a man who almost died doing his best for his country! So it was then that I got together with a couple of mates of mine, Brownie and McCaughney, to organise a welcome home fit for a war hero.

When the big day arrived we was good and ready. There was a nair of excitement at the railway station, people gathering around to see what a real war hero's VD looked like. Slowly, the old South West Mail pulls in, grinding to a halt. Weakly, me Dad stepped from the carriage and that's when I gave the signal and down fell our banner:

WELCOME HOME
PRIVATE MARSH ... VD!

Well, things got a bit confusing after that. Dad fainted. Mum broke down again. Some people cheered. Others laughed. The Salvation Army packed up and went home and Aunt Nell, well, she took me to her place ... for a whole month.

Then when I got home, Dad wouldn't tell me how he got the VD. And even to this day I've never seen what it looks like. But that's me dad. Very humble. Unselfish. And he never boasts about his great war feats.

Twenty-five Penguins

(Trucking Stories)

A few years back I had a mate who, for the sake of any possible legal ramifications, I'll call Bob. Bob had worked at Perth Zoo since he was a teenager and in his later years he'd risen to the lofty heights of being their despatch and acquisitions officer. That job made him responsible for the welfare and transportation of the animals. Like, if an elephant or something needed a break from the stress of being ogled at by bucketloads of human beings and had to be moved elsewhere, it was Bob's job to sort it out. Or, on the other hand, if animals were being received into the zoo from elsewhere, that was also Bob's job. Anyhow, at his retirement dinner, Bob related the story of the twenty-five penguins.

It went something like this. Around one Christmas, Bob had received a top priority notice that there were twenty-five penguins arriving in Western Australia by sea. I forget where they were coming from just now, but they had to be picked up at the Fremantle Port as soon as the ship had been unloaded, and transported to Perth Zoo for resettlement. Being the middle of summer and as hot as buggery, Bob decided to organise a refrigerated van to take these twenty-five penguins from the port to the zoo. Over the years he'd dealt with one particular transport company that he knew were not only extremely reliable, but more importantly, they had refrigerated vans of all shapes and sizes. I won't mention the transport company's name but they were a well-known mob in WA who not only delivered locally, but throughout the entire state, right into the outback, into some of the more far-flung communities. Anyhow, to coincide with the docking of the ship, Bob booked this transport mob for a 10 a.m. pick-up, the following morning, which was a Tuesday.

'No worries,' said the woman who organised such things. 'We'll have a small refrigerated van at the port just before 10 a.m.'

'Good,' he said. 'I'll ring through the pick-up details as soon as I get them.'

Anyhow, first thing on the Monday morning — the day before the Tuesday pick-up — Bob got a call from the people at the Fremantle Port. 'The ship's arrived early. The penguins have been unloaded on Dock 5. They're obviously not used to our Australian conditions so they're stressing with the heat. Can you get over here and pick them up straight away?'

Bugger.

So Bob was right onto the phone, back to the transport company. When he explained the situation, the woman who took the bookings said, 'Look, I'm very sorry, but with the extreme heat and it being so close to Christmas, all our refrigerated vans are out on other jobs and we won't have one free till much later on today.'

Shit, thought Bob. They could be dead by then. So he immediately went on to plan B. He jumped into one of the zoo's wire-caged utes and headed over to the port to pick up these heat-stressed penguins. When he got there, there was some sort of problem with the paperwork — something to do with quarantine matters — which delayed the pick-up for another hour. When that'd all been sorted out, he shot over to the pick-up point on Dock 5. And there were these twenty-five penguins, stuck out on a landing, crammed up in a small cage, looking worse for wear.

Bob's next problem was how to get them out of their cage on the landing and into the back of the ute, without stressing them any further by manhandling them one by one. There he was scratching his head over the matter when he had the thought that the wharfies must've somehow got them off the ship and into their cage. That's when he saw a small mob of wharfies standing just over the way a bit. So Bob approached one of the more enterprising-looking ones.

'Mate,' he said, 'have you got any suggestions as to how I might be able to coax these penguins out of their cage and into the back of the ute?'

'Easy,' the wharfie feller said. 'I'll just run a wide plank from the penguin's cage on the landing, onto the back of your ute. Then, all you have to do is to pretend you're their boss penguin and they'll follow you wherever you go.'

'How do I do that?' asked Bob.

'Well,' the wharfie said, 'just jump up onto the landing, stand in front of their cage, turn your baseball cap around, back to front, hold your arms tight to the sides of your body, splay your feet out as wide as you can, then, when I open up the door of their cage, just waddle along the plank, to the back of the ute and they'll follow you.'

'Yeah, right,' Bob said, thinking that the wharfie was having a lend of him.

'Well, have you got a better idea?' the wharfie replied. 'Because that's how we got them off the ship and into the cage.'

'Okay.'

So that's what Bob decided to do. He jumped up on the plank that the wharfie laid out for him. When he got to the front of the penguin's cage, he placed his cap around backwards, held his arms tight to his sides, and splayed his feet out as far as he could. Then, as soon as the wharfie opened up the cage, he started to waddle along the plank towards the back of the caged ute. And lo'n behold, as soon as the penguins saw Bob, they must've thought he was their long-lost Boss Penguin, because out they hopped and they followed him along the plank. When Bob got to the back of the ute, he stepped aside and the twenty-five penguins waddled straight past him and into the back of the ute.

The moment they were all inside the ute's cage, Bob shut the door. Job done.

'Thanks, mate,' he said to the wharfie and into the ute he jumped and he drove off, out of the port, until he got to the Canning Highway, over the bridge, did a leftie onto Saunders Road, then a rightie onto Labouchere Road and headed to the zoo.

The distance between the port and the zoo would've only been twenty kilometres or so, or half an hour's drive at the most. With it now nearing midday, the heat was furnace-like and so Bob was keen on getting these penguins rehoused as soon as humanly possible. But then, you wouldn't believe it, about half a kilometre from the zoo the bloody ute broke down.

Bugger it.

When Bob got out of the ute and checked on the penguins, they were not only sweating like pigs but they seemed none too happy that their new Boss Penguin had let them down — big-time. So he got straight onto the mobile phone and he rang the transport company. 'Any refrigerated vans available yet?'

'Sorry,' said the woman who was organising such things, 'they're all still out on jobs.'

So then he rang a few other transport companies. But none of them had a refrigerated van available. Not a one. Shit. So then he dialled up the RAC of WA — Royal Automobile Club of Western Australia — and explained the urgency of his predicament.

'Look, we're really sorry,' they said, 'but with the heat and all that, we've been overloaded with emergency calls and all our people are out on other jobs. We'll try our best to get someone there as soon as possible, but even then it could take anywhere up to a couple of hours.'

'Shit,' said Bob, 'they'll be dead by then.'

'Sorry, that's the best we can do.'

Bugger.

So, having run out of options, it looked like Bob was going to be stuck there with the stressed penguins for the next couple of hours, waiting for the bloody RAC to turn up.

And that's when he struck a bit of luck. Around the corner came this bloke. To give you some sort of idea, Bob described him as a vacant-looking kind of feller, five bob short of a quid — if you catch my drift — — who seemed like he was pretty much down and out. And that's when Bob had a brainwave.

'Excuse me, mate,' he said.

The feller looked at him vacantly. 'Yeah?'

'How'd yer like to earn twenty dollars?'

'What's the catch?' the feller asked.

'No catch at all,' Bob said. 'My car's broken down and I have to wait here for the RAC to come. All I'm asking you to do is to take these twenty-five penguins to the zoo for me.'

'How do I do that?' the vacant looking feller asked.

Bob said, 'It's easy. Just put my baseball cap on back to-front, hold your arms tight to your sides and splay your feet out as far as you can. Then, as soon as I open up the cage at the back of the ute, you start waddling in the direction of the zoo and they'll follow you.'

'Okay,' the feller said. 'Where's the twenty bucks?'

'Here,' said Bob and he handed over his baseball cap and a twenty-dollar note.

As soon as the feller stuffed the money into his pocket, he stuck Bob's cap on backwards, straightened his arms down by his side and he splayed his feet out. Then, when Bob opened the cage at the back of the ute and called out, 'Go,' the vacant-looking feller began to waddle off in the direction of the zoo. And lo'n behold the twenty-five penguins jumped straight out of the cage and they started to follow the feller up the road and around the corner, like he was the second coming of their previously disappointing Boss Penguin, Bob.

Anyhow, a couple of hours later Bob's still there waiting in the sweltering heat for the bloody RAC to turn up. Next thing, the vacant-looking feller comes waddling back around the corner. What's more, waddling along behind him are the twenty-five penguins.

'Hey,' Bob said, 'what the hell's going on?'

'Oh,' the feller said, 'Can you give me another twenty bucks?'

'Why's that?' said Bob.

'Well, I took the penguins to the zoo like you asked me to and they had such a good time there that they now want me to take them to the pictures.'

Squeaky the Stockman

(Flying Doctor Stories)

It was a hot, still Sunday in Nappa Merrie when Squeaky the stockman and his mates began maintenance work on an old Southern Cross windmill.

As usual, Squeaky somehow managed to draw the short straw and was given the job of climbing to the top of the windmill to oil the blades, grease the bearings, and so forth. There he was, working away, when a gust of wind came out of nowhere. The blades of the windmill suddenly spun into motion and Squeaky was knocked clean off the top platform. Down he fell in a flail of arms and legs.

For those who don't know, it's a good distance from the top of a windmill down to ground level. In this case, the only thing in the way was a water delivery pipe, about a yard or so off the ground.

The rest is history.

Some say that the pipe saved the wily stockman's life. But at what pains? I ask. Because a split second before impact Squeaky inexplicably parted his legs. Crunch! There he sat, motionless, astride that pipe, a loose leg dangling either side, his mouth rendered ajar, his eyes almost popped out of their sockets.

His workmates rushed to his side. 'How are yer, Squeaky?' they asked. 'Are yer all right, mate?'

But Squeaky didn't say a word. He tried to, mind you, but it was like there was an obstruction in his throat, somewhere just below his Adam's apple, stuck in his oesophagus.

'Ouch,' said his mates as they gently extricated him off the water delivery pipe. After they placed him on the ground, carefully, they called the Flying Doctor.

'Ouch.'

I don't know if you know or not, but Nappa Merrie's over in south-west Queensland so it took a while to fly out there. Then just as they'd settled Squeaky into the Nomad aircraft, another call came across the radio. This time a bloke down at Moomba had put a chunk of wood through his leg while chopping a log for the barbecue.

This left the doctor in an awkward situation. On one hand there was the bloke at Moomba who was in desperate need of help. On the other, there was Squeaky. Now Squeaky was a single bloke, a bit on the shy side with women like, but still and all there was the chance that he might want to settle down and raise a family some day. If so, an emergency operation might have to be carried out. Time was of the utmost importance and Moomba's in the north-east of South Australia, well out of the way.

'Well, Squeaky,' the doctor said, 'it's up to you, mate. Are you well enough to make the trip to Moomba before we head back to Broken Hill?'

At that point the wily stockman gave a sort of half-throatal gurgle which the doctor took to mean that he was okay to do the trip to Moomba.

'Brave decision,' the doctor said, before loading Squeaky up with pethidine, just in case the pain caught up with him somewhere along the way.

So they arrived in Moomba and picked up the bloke with the chunk of wood through his leg. The doctor gave the Moomba chap a shot of pethidine, plus an extra shot to Squeaky, just in case. As they were about to take off, lo and behold, another call came through. This one was from my wife who'd contacted them to say that I'd scalded my arm and was in need of emergency treatment.

Now the bloke with the lump of wood through his leg was no real problem. He could wait. But Squeaky ... Squeaky was a different matter.

'Well, Squeaky,' the doctor said, 'it's up to you, mate. Do you reckon you're well enough for another diversion before we head off back to Broken Hill?'

Squeaky gave another half-throatal gurgle, which the doctor took as an assurance that he was okay to do the trip from Moomba over to our property, just south of Broken Hill, before heading to the hospital.

'Brave decision,' the doctor said, then loaded Squeaky up with another dose of pethidine, just in case.

The doctor radioed ahead explaining the situation and asked if I could be ready to board the aeroplane as soon as it landed. So my wife drove me to the airstrip and the moment the plane cut its engines I jumped aboard. But when the pilot attempted to boot the engine of the Nomad, it was as dead as a doornail. He tried again. Same result. Dead silence. All we could hear was Squeaky letting go with one of his gurgles.

'We'll have to call out another plane,' said the pilot. 'The Nomad's buggered.'

So my wife drove us back to the homestead to escape the heat until the reserve plane arrived. There the doctor pumped some more pethidine into us all, just to tide us over.

Now perhaps it was because of the pethidine, I don't know, but soon after, Squeaky began to lighten up. Not that he could talk, mind you, but his throatal gurgles began to rise in pitch. So much so that by the time the reserve plane landed, Squeaky was sounding like he'd had a triple overdose of helium.

'Squeaky, yer getting squeakier and squeakier,' the pilot remarked.

Now I know it wasn't much of a joke. I guess you had to be there at the time, but it was enough to get Squeaky, me and the bloke with the lump of wood through his leg giggling like little kids, which was something we continued to do right up to the time we arrived at Broken Hill Hospital.

I don't know what happened to Squeaky the stockman after that. We sort of lost contact. He went one way and I went the other. So whether or not his family jewels needed rectifying, I don't know. But that was a fair while ago now and he still comes to mind occasionally — oddly enough, when I think about him I can't help but wince a little.

Paperwork

(Railway Stories)

Now, with the Victorian Railways, the head office was at Spencer Street station, and it became well known by us railway fellows as being either 'Bullshit Castle' or 'The Land of the Walking Dead'. And it was, fair dinkum. I mean, of course, this was well before computers, but all the paper-shufflers that ran around about that place shuffling paper was bloody unreal. You have no idea, all the red tape and bullshit that you had to put into written reports and so on and so forth. It almost blew your nose. Oh, everything was paperwork, paperwork, paperwork. So it was no wonder that we were always making up jokes and carrying on about all the different ways they could invent paperwork at Spencer Street.

I remember one joke. It went like this: there was a beautiful, young blonde lady waiting at Spencer Street station to catch a train to Ballarat. Anyway, she had the need to visit the Ladies Waiting Room and, when she went into the waiting room, she saw this brand-new set of fancy scales. So she went over to the scales and she noticed that it read on the top, 'One Penny Will Read Your Fortune'.

'This sounds alright,' she said. So she stood on the scales and she put a penny in the slot and the scales printed out this piece of paper which read, 'You are eight stone two pounds, blonde, young and beautiful, and you're about to pass wind.'

Well, most of that was spot-on, she had to agree. But as for passing wind, well, that seemed a bit far-fetched. But then, much to her surprise, the instant she stepped off the scales she farted.

'Well,' she thought, 'if the scales knew I was going to pass wind, I wonder what else they can reveal.' So to find out, she jumped back on the scales and she stuck another penny in the slot and this time the scales printed out, 'You are still eight stone two pounds, blonde, young and beautiful. You have just passed wind and now you're about to have wild, passionate sex.'

Well, that was completely impossible. I mean, after all, she was in the Ladies Waiting Room in the centre of Spencer Street station. But then, who should walk into the waiting room by mistake? None other than the most handsome bloke this lady had ever seen. And this woman, she took one look at this bloke and this bloke, he took one look at this woman and before either of them realised it, there they were, in one of the cubicles, having wild, passionate sex.

Then when this fellow had left, the woman staggered out of the cubicle and she went back over to the scales and she rummaged through her purse until she found another penny. So she stood on the scales and put the penny in the slot and the scales printed out, 'You're still eight stone two pounds, blonde, young and beautiful, but with all your farting about and fucking around you've just missed your last train to Ballarat.'

And, oh God, we laughed at that one. But I mean, with all the paperwork they made us do, as I said, it was just bloody unreal. Another time, and this is true, when I was at Hamilton all the animals like the dogs, cats and birds and things had to be carried in the guard's van, not in the carriage. And I can tell you, there have been some disasters, what with dogs falling out of the guard's van door, birds gone missing — presumably flown the coop — cats scratching you and so forth and so on. Anyhow, after a few of these accidents had filtered through to Spencer Street, some enterprising paper-shuffler came up with the bright idea that at each change of crew, which was every 60 miles or so, the new guard had to fill out a continuing report as to the current condition and welfare of every animal in his van.

Anyway, one time, someone sent a dog over from South Australia and it somehow died before it crossed the border. Then at Nhill there was a change over of crew and that's where the Victorian guard discovered that this dog had died. So he wrote on his report, 'Dog dead at Nhill'.

So that was okay. Then at the next change of crew, say, at Horsham, the new guard checked the animals and, when he found the dead dog, he checked back over the previous guard's report then wrote on his report, 'Exact same dog still dead at Horsham.'

Then at the next change of crew, the new guard checked all the animals, saw the dead dog, checked the previous reports and wrote, 'Exact same dog remains still dead at Ararat. Rigor mortis set in. No hope of revival.'

Anyhow, this happened all the way down the line until the train got into Spencer Street, where the animals were finally unloaded and a completion-of-journey report had to be filled out. And when that final report was handed in to the paper-shuffler at Spencer Street, the signing-off guard, who was a bit of a dag, had written, 'Exact same dead dog still remains dead at Spencer Street. No hope of revival. Spirit risen. Carcass rotting. Amen.'

More Paperwork

(Bush Funeral Stories)

A while back, up in Darwin, there was this very officious parking inspector. Very officious he was. He was extremely well known around town. Some of your Top End readers may even remember being nabbed by him. And, oh, he'd grab you for anything. Three seconds over the parking limit and you'd be gone.

Anyway, outside one of the local Darwin churches there was a sign that read along the lines of:

NO STANDING EXCEPT FOR FUNERAL VEHICLES

The thing was, if the local priest was in a hurry and wanted to pick something up from the church, it was an ideal place for him to park his car for a minute or two while he zipped inside to grab whatever he was after. But just about every time he parked there to go into the church, when he came back there'd be this parking inspector, standing there, writing out a parking violation ticket.

'Gee, mate,' the priest would say, 'I only just popped in for a tick to grab something.'

'Doesn't matter,' would come the reply. 'Read the sign. It says, "No standing except for funeral vehicles".'

'But I'm not blocking any traffic,' the priest would plead. 'There's no funeral in progress and, if there was, surely I'd be the first person to know about it.'

'Sorry,' the parking inspector would say as he was slapping the ticket onto the priest's windscreen, 'it's too bloody late, mate. I've already done the paperwork.'

'Shit,' the priest would mutter under his breath. But there was no way he could talk the parking inspector out of it. The paperwork had already been done and so the parking fine had to be paid.

Now, as it transpired, this parking inspector died. I believe it was from a heart attack or something. And as it also transpired, this priest drew the short straw among his fellow clergy to officiate at the parking inspector's funeral. It wasn't a cremation, it was a burial. Only a handful of people turned up, and the vast majority of those probably only came along just to make sure that the parking inspector was dead and buried.

Anyhow, after the service, they headed out to the cemetery for the burial. Just as the parking inspector was being lowered into his grave there came this scream from within his coffin: 'I'm not dead! I'm not dead! Let me out! Let me out!'

At hearing that, the priest broke out into a wry smile. He gave a meaningful glance to those in attendance, then he leant forward, sucked some air through his teeth, and muttered down at the coffin, 'Too bloody late, mate. I've already done the paperwork.'

Train Hit by Man

(Flying Doctor Stories)

Now Barton's an interesting place. Ever heard of it? Not many have. It's a small railway siding out in the Nullarbor, at the start of the world's longest straight stretch of track, leading from there to eternity, then further on to Kalgoorlie. There's bugger-all there these days apart from millions of flies and a fluctuating population of between one and six, and that's counting the stray horses and camels. Even for the most imaginative of real estate agents, the best that could be said about Barton is that it's 'nestled comfortably among endlessly rolling red sandhills'. Beyond that you'd be scratching for compliments.

Back a few years ago when the railways scaled down, there was an old German bloke by the name of Ziggie, a railway worker of some sort, a fettler maybe. Anyway, with all the kerfuffle Ziggie decided to retire after thirty years on the job. But instead of retiring to the Big Smoke of Port Augusta like the rest of the workers out that way did, he thought, 'Vell, bugger it. I've no family, novere to go. Zo as-t long as-t zee Tea and Sugar Train still delivers vater and supplies, I'll stay in zee Barton.'

The trouble was that he'd been left with no place to live. So for the next couple of years he wandered up and down the track with a wheelbarrow picking up the sleepers which had been cast aside during track maintenance. And out of those he built a huge three-roomed bunker, complete with a patio where he could sit and sip on his Milo and watch the sun set over the endlessly rolling red sandhills.

Now you may think that the mention of him sipping on Milo, instead of a gin and tonic or a cold beer or something of a more refreshing nature, was a slip of the tongue. But it wasn't. Old Ziggie drank nothing but Milo. In actual fact, his staple diet was Milo, oranges, potatoes and, as the strong rumour had it, canned dog food. Yep, you heard it right ... canned dog food. Canned dog food, Milo, oranges and potatoes for breakfast, dinner and tea, and a good brand too, mind you.

So Ziggie settled down to life at Barton along with his seven dogs. And he's had a good many more than seven dogs in his time because he keeps a collection of their skulls. If you go to Ziggie's place, the one made out of discarded railway sleepers, there they are, all these dog skulls lined up, along with the empty cans of dog food and the empty Milo tins which he uses as an antenna for his short-wave radio.

But other than being the collector of dog skulls and a connoisseur of fine dog food, oranges, potatoes and Milo, old Ziggie just happens to be one of the best informed individuals that you're ever likely to meet. As you might imagine, there's not too much for him to do out at Barton except to listen to his short-wave radio, which he does day in, day out. Ziggie knows more about the goings-on of the world than anyone I know. What's more, he has an opinion on any subject and if he doesn't he'll soon make one up.

So life's a pretty solitary affair out at Barton which, in turn, causes the Bartonites to get mighty suspicious when a blow-in lobs into town. Not that many do, mind you. Maybe one or two each decade or so. But just enough for the locals, including Ziggie, to have formed the solid impression that the rest of the world is inhabited by ... weirdos.

And so it was that one of the locals wandered out at the crack of dawn one day and discovered that some bloke, a blow-in type, had appeared from God-knows-where in the middle of the night and had been bowled over by the Tea and Sugar Train as it was pulling into the siding. The evidence was right there for all to see. There was this complete stranger, sprawled under the front of the train, out to the world, comatose in fact, with his head split open, stinking of grog and looking on death's door.

'Typical of these blow-ins, aye,' someone muttered, to which there was total agreement.

Of course, the train driver was upset. But as he said, 'How the hell could I have bowled someone over when the train only travels at snail's pace?' And there were those that saw his point of view. See, it's been rumoured that the driver of the Tea and Sugar Train wasn't given a timetable upon departure from Port Augusta. Instead, he was handed a calendar because it really didn't matter when he arrived in Kalgoorlie, just as long as he did, at some stage of the year.

Naturally, not long after Ziggie had appeared on the scene he'd come up with a theory about the accident. He reckoned that the train hadn't hit the blow-in, but that the reverse had occurred. In fact, upon closer inspection, Ziggie deduced that the bloke had been so pissed when he'd staggered out of the sandhills and into Barton at some ungodly hour of the night that he'd walked headlong into the stationary train. Crack! Split his head open and down he'd gone like a sack of spuds, right under the front wheels, and hadn't moved a muscle since.

After much discussion the Flying Doctor from over in Port Augusta was called. And while the blow-in lay prostrate under the train, the discussion raged as to whatever reason the bloke might have had to be wandering around the desert in the middle of the night. And so the discussion continued right up until the locals saw the plane land. Then they put a hold on things while a ute was sent out to pick up the doctor and the nurse.

It was during the brief respite that Ziggie organised the making of a bush stretcher. The reasoning behind that was to save precious time so the blow-in could be placed into the back of the ute as soon as the doctor had checked him over. So they slung a bit of canvas around a couple of bits of gidgee then rolled the unconscious bloke onto the stretcher.

When the doctor arrived he went through the full medical procedure. 'This bloke's in an extremely critical condition,' he concluded. 'So, fellers, when you pick up the stretcher take it nice and easy.'

Now, constructing a house out of railway sleepers may have been one of old Ziggie's fortes but making a stretcher out of a strip of canvas and a couple of bits of gidgee apparently wasn't. Because, when they lifted the stretcher, the canvas gave way and the blow-in went straight through and hit his head on the railway track with an almighty thud.

'Holy Jesus,' someone said, 'we've killed him fer sure.'

But almost before those words had been spoken, the blow-in miraculously snapped back into consciousness. What's more, to everyone's surprise, particularly the doctor's, the bloke sat bolt upright. He took one look at the menagerie of faces gawking down at him, then a quick glance out at the endlessly rolling red sandhills.

'Where the bloody hell am I?' he squawked.

'Barton,' came the reply, to which the blow-in got up, shook his head and staggered off down the track, leaving the doctor mystified and locals only more reassured at the weirdness of humankind in the outside world. This, of course, included Ziggie, who wandered back home to tuck into a nice hearty breakfast.

Elliston, SA

(Outback Towns and Pubs)

I'd say it would've been around the end of June 1972 that a mate and I went over to the west coast of South Australia to do a spot of fishing. Anyhow, we ended up at a beautiful little place on the Eyre Peninsula, called Elliston. From memory, I think the pub we stayed in was called the Elliston Hotel.

Now, I've found out a couple of quite interesting things about Elliston, the first being that Elliston's one of the very few places in Australia that's been named after a writer. Her name was Ellen Liston. She was a governess over there during the 1850s and she had a few books published. So in gratitude to her it was originally known as Ellie's Town and that later got changed to Elliston. Then something else I discovered was that, back before it was named Ellie's Town, it was known as Waterloo Bay, and that name came about after a mob of Aborigines were herded up to the top of a cliff by some white settlers and given the choice, 'Either jump or be shot.' Then, from that incident, one of the white fellers concluded how the Aborigines had met their Waterloo. Hence the name Waterloo Bay, and the bay's still known as that.

Anyhow, all that aside, I've got a story about our stay at Elliston. See, when we went to the bar, my mate kindly offered to buy me a glass of Grandfather Port. Now, up until that stage, I'd never had a taste of that particular port before and, mind you, I've never had a taste of it since. So we had this glass of Grandfather Port then, as what happens, we had a few more and at some stage of the evening we got talking to the publican.

'So yer like yer Grandfather Port, ay?' he said.

My mate said, 'Yes I do, very much. It's a bit expensive but it's a nice drop.'

Anyway, the publican says, 'Well, you and yer liking for Grandfather Port reminds me of an old story I was told, from many years ago.'

'Yeah,' we said.

And he told us a story that went something like this: see, pre-myxomatosis there was an old rabbiter who'd set up camp somewhere out of Elliston and he scraped out a meagre living by selling skins to the local dealer plus the occasional carcasses to the butcher and to some of the locals. Then, like so many did back in those days, this feller kept a shotgun close at hand, just in case he came upon a snake or got attacked by a dingo. Actually, rumour had it that, around Elliston at the time this story took place, there was a particularly vicious rogue dingo who'd been known to have, and I quote, 'ripped a few people to shreds' as the publican described it.

Anyhow, one day the old rabbiter had come into town to sell his skins and carcasses. Now, something I forgot was that the only transport this feller had was an old pushbike. That's all, an old pushbike. So he'd strung the carcasses across the handlebars and down along the pipe thing that goes between the steering column and the seat, and he'd stacked the rabbit skins in a wheat bag and tied it down, tight, on the carry-frame at the back of his bike. Then he slung his shotgun over his shoulder and off into Elliston he pedalled. It was a couple of hours ride or something. This was in the middle of summer and so he was pretty parched by the time he arrived in town and he was even more parched by the time he'd gone around and sold all his skins and his few carcasses. But by now he's got some money in his pocket and so he ends up in the pub.

'What'll yer have?' says the bloke behind the bar.

The old rabbiter says, 'Oh, I'm pretty flush so I might have a glass'a that Grandfather Port, over there.'

So the barman poured the old rabbiter a glass of Grandfather Port, which he downed. Then he downed another one. Then another. And by midnight this old rabbiter's blown all his hard-earned money on Grandfather Port, so he slurs, 'See yer,' to the barman and he staggers outside, slings his shotgun over his shoulder, gets on his pushbike and he heads out of town the long way. By 'the long way' I mean that the bike was zigzagging so badly from one side of the road to the other that, by the time he would've gotten back to his camp he would've almost covered twice the distance.

So there he was, snaking his way down this old dirt track. It's a nice moonlit night, but it's all getting the better of him. He's not seeing too well. In fact, you could liken him to being as blind as a bat, plus he's starting to feeling as crook as a dog. So he decides to lay down beside the dirt track to sleep it off. And it was while he was snoring away he thought he heard a dingo growl and, when he sprung awake, there, just a few feet from his face, were these two bright shining eyes. It's the rogue dingo! he thinks, so he grabs his shotgun and he gives it both barrels, straight between the eyes. 'Boom ... Boom.' There's this hell of a racket, then all's quiet.

'Gotcha,' he said, then he went back to sleep.

It wasn't until mid-morning, with the sun pelting down, that the old rabbiter woke, with a hell of a hangover. The worst he's ever had in his entire life. 'I'll never touch another bloody drop of that bloody Grandfather Port again,' he swears. Then he recalls shooting the rogue dingo. He has a look around. But, no, not a sign. No dead dingo. No blood. Not even a paw print.

'Well, bugger me.' Then it was only when he went to get on his pushbike that he saw that the handlebars had been shot, clean off. So he must've woken up in the night and seen the moonlight reflecting off the handlebars and, in his drunken state, thinking they were the eyes of the rogue dingo, he'd inadvertently blown his own handlebars off.

So that's the story. Now, whether that's true or not, I don't know, but the publican was dead right about one thing: a night on the Grandfather Port gives you one hell of a hangover and so, like the old rabbiter, I swore that I'd never touch a drop of the stuff again.

Where's Me Hat?

(Flying Doctor Stories)

We were flying out to Tibooburra to do a clinic one day when we received an urgent request to divert to Noocundra, in south-western Queensland. Someone had been severely burnt. The odd thing was, though, the chap who put through the call couldn't stop laughing. Naturally, we thought that it mustn't have been too serious, and we said so. But the chap, the one who was laughing, was adamant that the victim was badly burnt and, yes, it was anything but a laughing matter, which he was, if that makes any sense.

As the story unfolded, it'd been a stifling hot day in Noocundra and a few of the locals were in the pub attempting to escape the heat. The problem was that a large tiger snake was thinking along similar lines. It appeared in the pub and had a look around. But when it saw the accumulated gathering, it decided that it didn't like the company and headed off to the next best place it could think of, that being the outside toilet, one of those long-drop types. So out of the pub the tiger snake slithered, down the track a bit, into the outside toilet, and disappeared down the long-drop where it was nice and cool.

Now this chap saw where the snake had gone and he came up with the bright idea of incinerating it. He downed his drink, put on his hat, went and got a gallon of petrol, wandered back through the pub, down the track a bit, into the outside toilet, and tossed the fuel down the long-drop where the snake was. The problem was, after he'd tossed the petrol down the long-drop, he searched through all his pockets and couldn't find his matches. So he wandered back inside the pub.

'Anyone seen me matches?' he asked.

As I said, it was a very hot, still day in Noocundra, stinking hot, in actual fact. So after he found his matches, he thought that he may as well have another drink before he went back outside and sorted out the snake. Meantime the petrol fumes were rising up from out of the long-drop and, with there not being a breath of a breeze to disperse them, the toilet soon became nothing short of a gigantic powder keg.

After the chap had downed his drink, he grabbed his matches and put his hat back on. 'I'll be back in a tick,' he said. Then he wandered outside, down the track a bit, in the direction of the toilet. Without having a clue as to what he was in for, he walked into the toilet and took out a match.

'Goodbye, snake,' he said, and struck the match over the long-drop.

There are those from the outlying districts who go so far as to say that they felt the reverberations of the ensuing explosion. I don't know about that, but one thing's for sure, it certainly put the wind up the blokes who were hanging around the bar of the Noocundra pub. Such was the instantaneous impact of the blast that they didn't even have the time to down their drinks before they hit the floor. Mind you, that's only a rumour because, knowing some of the chaps out that way, no matter what the emergency they always finish their drinks before taking any action, even if it's a reflex action.

Still, you've got to feel sorry for the chap who went up in the sheet of flames. Critically burnt he was. Left standing over what had once been the pub's long-drop toilet with his clothes smouldering away. Stank to high heaven he did. It affected the chap's hearing too. Deaf as a post he was for a good while. And the shock, poor bloke. Even by the time we got there he was still as dazed as a stunned mullet.

As for his hat, it's never been found.

The Prick and the Emu

(Trucking Stories)

I'm ringing you up on behalf of a mate of mine, Bob McManus, who wants to remain anonymous. Which is why he's got me speaking to you, kind of as a third party once removed, so to speak. That's because he was involved in the following incident, up to his eyeballs, and he reckons that if The Prick finds out who done it, his life might not be worth living. What's more, to further distance himself even more, Bob's made the strong suggestion that, when you write up his story, you should change his name to an alias like Ted or something like that.

Good. Okay. Thanks.

So anyhow, as Bob — alias Ted — tells it, there was this arsehole of a truck driver that he and his trucking mates had nicknamed as The Prick. Now, I'm not certain how the nickname came about because Bob — alias Ted — has made himself currently indisposed. So I'm just presuming that The Prick got his nickname from being a prickly sort of bloke. That's my take on it anyhow, because Bob — alias Ted — reckons that The Prick was one of them real unlikeable fellers who was always out to pick a fight or an argument, or both of them at once. Like, if there was no hint of rain on the horizon and the temperature was hovering in the mid-bloody-twenties and there was a deep blue sky with the sun shining and someone said to The Prick, 'Gee, it's a good lookin' day, ay?' The Prick would say right back at them, 'No it ain't,' just like that. And if you pushed him any further on the matter, he'd either want to argue his case or want to settle the matter out the back of the pub or the roadhouse or wherever, man to man.

So anyway, now to the story. The way Bob — alias Ted — told me to tell it to you was that, a group of truckies had had enough of The Prick. This was back when a few of them were doing the south–north run up through Bourke, Cunnamulla, Charleville, on to Barkie — Barcaldine — then over to Longreach and on to the Isa. That's Mount Isa, if you didn't know. Now, just out of Cunnamulla there was apparently this roadhouse where the fellers would occasionally meet up for a meal and a chat. So this night they're all in there and who should turn up — none other than The Prick.

He walks in.

'How yer goin'?' they say, trying to sound nice and bright.

'Up ter shit,' he replies.

'Oh, that's good. Nothin' unusual then,' they say.

The Prick ignores them and he goes over to the counter where he fronts Mary. Mary ran the place. She'd apparently been there for years. Bob — alias Ted — described her as being 'one of them real gems who got on well with the vast majority of the truckies, and got on even better with a few of the others', if you catch my drift.

'Give us the usual,' The Prick barks out to her.

'And what might that be, sir?' Mary replies, in a soft-mannered, polite tone, just to stir The Prick up. Plus he apparently hated being called 'sir'.

'Fuck off,' he said. 'The usual. The mixed grill 'n make sure the meat's cooked. Not like yer done it last time when it came out of yer kitchen lookin' like it were fresh roadkill.'

'Yes, sir,' says Mary, stirring him up a bit more.

''N don't forget the coffee. Strong. Not like the piss yer served up ter me last bloody time.'

'Yes, sir,' says Mary, stirring him up even a bit more.

So then The Prick goes and he squats himself down at a table where Bob — alias Ted — and a few of the other truckie fellers were sitting. Apparently he always did that because he knew there were better odds of getting involved in an argument. Which, of course, he does. Bob — alias Ted — forgets what the actual argument was about this time. But it could've been anything from the weather to the road conditions, to politics to religion, sport or even tiddlywinks. Anything. It didn't matter. So before long there's this verbal barney going on over whatever it was. Eventually The Prick comes to the conclusion that everyone else is completely wrong on the subject and he's the only one who's completely right — or so he thinks.

Now, on this particular trip, The Prick was apparently taking a load of mining machinery from somewhere down south, up through Bourke and Cunnamulla then on to the Isa. That's Mount Isa, if you didn't already know. So, as they all did, when they were on the northern leg of their run, he'd pulled up at the roadhouse with his truck facing north. By doing that, after he'd finished his mixed grill and coffee and he'd had a gutful of arguing with everyone, all he had to do was to walk outside, jump in his truck, fire it up and away he'd go, continuing north, on his way up to the Isa.

So The Prick gets his mixed grill, which Mary had cooked rare, just to stir the bastard up even more. Then she serves him a piss-weak cup of coffee, just like he doesn't like it. And while the argument then turns to what a shitheap of a roadhouse this is and how Mary's the worst cook ever to grace this earth, Bob — alias Ted — sneaks out through the back toilet area, and he goes over to The Prick's truck. Now, apparently, like most truckies are in the habit of doing, the keys have been left in the ignition. So Bob — alias Ted — jumps in, see. Then, as the argument's reaching boiling point inside the roadhouse, Bob — alias Ted — takes The Prick's truck in an anti-clockwise circuit around the roadhouse before he parks it back in its spot. Though this time, instead of leaving the truck facing in a northerly direction, as it previously had been, Bob — alias Ted — parks it facing south, heading back toward Bourke, which is where The Prick had just come from.

So anyway, after The Prick scoffs down his meal, he tells everyone what a mob of arseholes they are. When everyone says that he's wrong and that he's the arsehole and not them, he then invites them out the back of the roadhouse, to sort things out once and for all. When there are no takers, he calls them a mob of gutless wonders. Then he leaves half his coffee and he goes over to Mary to pay his bill.

'That's the worst fuckin' meal I've ever had,' he says before adding, ''N yer coffee's shit.'

'Yes, sir,' says Mary, handing him back his change.

''N don't call me "sir",' he adds, to which Mary replies, 'No, sir.'

With that, The Prick's really riled up. Of course, by now Bob — alias Ted — has returned back to the fold after his little escapade and he reckons that there was steam coming out of The Prick's ears. So anyway, with no one to have a stoush with, The Prick storms out of the roadhouse.

'See yer later, mate,' the truckies sing out.

'Fuck off, the lot of yers,' replies The Prick. 'Yer nothing but a pack'a bastards.'

And as Bob — alias Ted — and his mates gather around the window of the roadhouse, they watch as The Prick jumps into the cab of his truck, turns the key to ignite the engine and off he drives. And the last Bob — alias Ted — and his truckie mates saw of The Prick that night was his tail-lights disappearing in a southerly direction, down the Mitchell Highway, heading back toward Bourke.

So there you go. And now to a joke sort of thing that Bob — alias Ted — wants me to tell you. It's one that he tells anyone and everyone who's willing to lend him their ear. You may have already heard it, or versions of it, quite a few times over. But anyhow, this is how it goes.

An Aussie truck driver walks into an outback roadhouse. For the sake of the story, let's say that the roadhouse is in Cunnamulla. Anyhow, tagging along behind the truckie is a fully grown emu.

Mary, the waitress, says to the truckie, 'And what would you like to order?'

After the truckie checks over the menu, he says, 'A hamburger 'n chips 'n a Coke, thanks.' Then he turns to the emu and says, 'And what would you like?'

'Sounds good to me,' says the emu. 'I'll have the same.'

'Okay,' says Mary. 'Take a seat and I'll bring it over in a tick,' and she disappears into the kitchen.

A short time later Mary returns with the order. 'There you go,' she says, 'two hamburgers, two serves of chips and a couple of Cokes.'

'How much?' asks the truckie.

'That'll be nine dollars forty, thanks,' replies Mary.

'Okay,' says the truckie and he fishes around in his pocket and he pulls out the exact change. 'There yer go' he says, 'Nine dollars 'n forty cents,' and he hands it over to Mary.

A week or so later the truckie and the emu come into the roadhouse again. It's the same thing. Mary asks what he wants to eat. He says, 'Hamburger, chips 'n a Coke, thanks.' Then he turns to the emu and says, 'And what would you like?'

'Sounds good to me,' says the emu. 'I'll have the same.'

'Okay,' says Mary. 'Take a seat and I'll bring it over in a tick,' and she disappears into the kitchen.

A short time later she returns with the order. 'There you go,' she says. 'Two hamburgers, two serves of chips and a couple of Cokes. That's a total of nine dollars forty, thanks.'

'Okay,' says the truckie and he fishes around in his pocket and he pulls out the exact change. 'There yer go' he says, 'nine dollars 'n forty cents,' and he hands it over to Mary.

Anyhow, this becomes a routine. Every time the truckie and the emu come into the Cunnamulla roadhouse they go through the same rigmarole. 'Two hamburgers, two serves of chips and a couple of Cokes.' And the truckie hands over the exact change, nine dollars and forty cents, every time.

Then one night the two enter; the truckie followed by the emu.

'The usual?' asks Mary.

'No thanks,' says the truckie, 'it's Friday night, so I might have the fish 'n chips with a side salad and a Sprite.'

'And the same for me,' pipes up the emu.

So Mary heads off into the kitchen and a short time later she brings out two servings of fish and chips, along with two side salads and a couple of Sprites.

'What's the damage?' asks the truckie.

'That'll be twenty-two fifty, thanks,' says Mary.

And once again the truckie fishes around in his pocket and he places the exact change down on the table: twenty-two dollars and fifty cents.

By this stage, Mary can't hold back her curiosity. 'Excuse me, mate,' she says, 'how do you manage to pull out the exact change from your pocket every single time?'

'Well, love,' says the truckie, 'a few years ago, I was cleaning out the truck shed 'n I came across a dirty old lamp. While I was cleaning it, a genie appeared 'n offered me two wishes.'

'And what did you wish for?' asks Mary.

'Well,' said the truckie, 'my first wish was that, if I ever had to pay for anything whatsoever, I'd just be able to put my hand in my pocket and the exact amount of money would always be there.'

'That's brilliant,' says Mary. 'Most people would ask for a million dollars. But with a wish like that you'll be able to afford anything you want, for as long as you live.'

'That's right,' said the truckie, 'whether it's a litre of milk or a Rolls-Royce, the exact change will always be there.'

'And so, what's with the emu?' asks Mary.

The truckie pauses. 'Well,' he sighs, 'my second wish was for a tall bird with a big arse and long legs, who agrees with everything I say.'

Boom, boom.

And Bob — alias Ted — says thanks for the lend of your ear.

Been Around, Done a Thing or Two

(More Flying Doctor Stories)

I'm seventy years old actually, and I've retired. I was in the car game for forty-five years but, oh, back a while now, I had a bit of a heart turn and I was in Chinchilla Hospital. Chinchilla's west of Brisbane, between Dalby and Roma. Anyway, after four days, the Flying Doctors came out and they flew me to Brisbane. So really, I just wanted to say an extra thank you to the Royal Flying Doctor Service, you know, not only for how they helped me but, for all us bush people, especially those that live out in the real remote areas. They'd be done without them.

So that's all I was going to say and then I was going to tell you a little story about my dad. Dad used to be a drover. Out through the west of Queensland he was commonly known as 'Flash Jack McIntyre'. You might've heard of him. I used to go out droving with him too, right out Charleville way, all around throughout that district: Tambo, Augathella, Cunnamulla, Eulo and all them places. One of my brothers also used to be out that way. He was a Senior Sergeant of Police: Neil McIntyre.

But long before he joined the police force, Neil and my other brother, Duncan, and myself — my name's Noel — we all done a stint or three out the west, droving with Dad and other fellers. It was an experience, I can tell you. As a matter of fact, do you know Howard Hobbs? From memory he's the Local Member for Maranoa. Well, we used to do a lot of droving for his father. I think his name was also Howard Hobbs, and they lived at Tambo.

Oh, there's stacks of stories I could tell. It just goes on and on. But see, if someone asked me to go camping today, I'd say, 'No thank you, very much.' Because, you know, when you were out droving, it was a tough old life. You hardly saw anyone and you didn't eat very well and you only had a wash every time you got to a creek or a bore drain. Don't get me wrong, it was good experience but it certainly made me realise the good things in life.

Anyhow, see, Dad was out droving one time and, back in those days, the telephone lines they had were only bush telephone lines. You know, they were just a length of old wire cable that ran between properties and properties, and they were only strung up loosely between one old rickety wooden pole to another or, if they could find a tree, it was hung from one tree to another tree, that sort of thing; pretty rough. Anyhow, Dad used to hang a leading-line between the horse he was riding and the pack-saddle horse. So he was going along, nice and steady, when a telephone line got caught in the pack-saddle and the packhorse shied and it threw the pack-saddle back and it hit Dad fair on the mouth. Then, as Dad got hit, he flinched and his spurs dug into his horse and it leaped and bolted off. And that's how Dad ended up in Charleville Hospital, where he had quite a lot of stitches in his mouth and all that.

Now, what you've got to understand is that this was fifty odd years ago and, back then, there were lots of people who were living out in those real remote places who'd never even been into a big town. Like, they were born in the bush and that's where they stayed for the whole of their lives, out in the bush.

Anyhow, the nursing people in at the Charleville Hospital were telling Dad about this old-timer who'd worked out on a remote station property. He'd never been out of the bush so he'd most certainly never seen a town as big as Charleville, which meant it was a dead cert that he'd never been in a hospital before.

Anyhow, he'd been pretty badly bunged up. I'm not real sure just why now. It might've even been a riding accident or something. But the thing was that it happened away out in one of the real remote areas and the Flying Doctors had to go out and bring him back into Charleville for treatment.

Well, this old-timer arrived at Charleville Hospital — as I said he was pretty bunged up — and the nurses said, 'We're going to have to take you for X-rays.'

Now, of course, this old-timer didn't have a clue what an X-ray was so he started to get real worried. 'Will it hurt?' he asked.

'No,' they said, 'You won't even know you've had one.'

But that didn't seem to ease this old-timer's worries. For starters, he was a bit suspicious about putting all his trust in these strange, city-type people. To his liking they talked too fast and, anyway, you'd have to be mad to want to live in a big place like Charleville. So he was really nervy. Then by the time they got him into a wheelchair, he was even more nervy. He'd never been in one of those neither. As they were wheeling him down the corridor, he was so bad that he was sweating.

By the time they pressed the button for the lift he was in a real panic. Then, while they were standing around, waiting for the lift to come, they noticed that the old-timer's knuckles had gone white from gripping so hard onto the wheelchair.

'It'll all be over very soon, sir,' they said, trying to reassure the old-timer.

So the lift arrived and they rolled this old feller into the lift and they pressed the button to take the lift to the second floor of the hospital, which was where the X-ray Department was. Then just as they wheeled him out of the lift on the second floor, the old-timer let go a big sigh.

'Are you alright, Mr so-and-so?' they asked.

'Well, you were right,' he replied. 'Isn't it bloody marvellous how they do X-rays, eh? That didn't even hurt a bit.'

And Dad was laughing his head off about this because, you know, Dad had lived. He'd been down to Brisbane and all those places, where they've got lifts and escalators and all that. So he'd been around, done a thing or two, as they say. But, you know, back fifty years or so a lot of those old-timers away out in the backblocks of Queensland, they'd never seen a lift, and there was this old-timer, who'd never been out of the bush, well, he thought that the lift was an X-ray machine, didn't he.

Aramac, Qld

(Outback Towns and Pubs)

Aramac's about 100 miles north-east of Longreach; sort of in the south-west of Queensland, you could say. Nice and Slow, that's the kind of place it is.

Mind you, Aramac was one of the first towns out this way. A feller called William Landsborough and another feller called Nat Buchanan came through here in the late 1850s, when they were trying to find the lost explorer Ludwig Leichhardt. Oh, he was always getting lost, was Leichhardt. As mad as a hatter. Used to go charging around the camp swishing an old army sabre, with his saddle on his head as a helmet and wearing his saddle bags as if they was armour. As blind as a bat too, they say, so no wonder he kept getting lost. Oh, and another interesting thing about Aramac, that most people wouldn't know, is how it got its name. See, initially, Landsborough named the local creek after the first Premier of Queensland, R.R. McKenzie. So it was known as the R.R. Mac Creek. Then, over time, with lazy speech and all that, it got turned into Aramac — a.r.a.m.a.c. Not too many people know that.

So there you go. I thought that might be of interest. Then, as time went by, Aramac turned into a big wool-producing area. There was a station about forty mile out of town, called Bowen Downs, and in its heyday they shore something like 360,000 sheep on the property. Actually, I believe it was the biggest station in the world, back in those days, and during the season it employed over 100 shearers; meaning it had about 100 stands. So, it was a pretty big operation.

But anyway, my story's got nothing to do with any of that because, see, in the 1950s people called Toby and Ruby Langdon kept the Marathon Hotel in Aramac. Then there was also a well-known local character who everyone knew as 'old Jack'. At that time, old Jack was looking after a small place about twenty mile from town and he had this old model car. Now, I'm not too sure what make the car was but every couple of weeks old Jack would drive this thing into Aramac to collect all the supplies and things he needed till the next time he came to town. Then after he'd done that he'd drive down to the Marathon Hotel for a few grogs before he headed off, back home. He enjoyed a drink.

So on this day, after collecting whatever stores he needed, old Jack drove his car down to the Marathon Hotel. It was about 3 o'clock in the afternoon and he pulled in, alongside the hotel, off the street, into the vacant area used for parking. He got out and he went into the pub for a few drinks. Toby was behind the bar this particular day. This is Toby Langdon.

'Give us a beer, Toby.'

'Yeah, Jack.'

Toby poured a beer. 'Here yer go.'

'Thanks.'

'So how's things, Jack?'

'Not bad.'

And so, while old Jack downed a few ales, they started having a bit of a chat about this, that and the weather and how damn lucky they were to be living in a nice quiet place like Aramac, where everyone got along pretty well and there was none of that terrible crime you read about happening in so many other places. There was no disagreement over that and so old Jack decided to have a few more ales to confirm it. But after a couple more hours, Toby could see that if the old feller was going to get home that night he'd better not serve him any more grog.

'I reckon that's about enough, ay, Jack?'

'Yeah, okay then,' said old Jack. 'I gotta be goin' anyway.'

So Jack left the bar. By now he's pretty unsteady on his feet so, just in case, Toby followed the old feller out of the bar. Then as old Jack made his way to the side of the hotel, where he'd parked his car, Toby stood at the top of the steps, just to keep an eye on him.

'See yer later,' old Jack called out to Toby. 'I'll be okay from here.'

Then, to Toby's surprise, instead of getting in the front seat of the car to drive off, old Jack opened the back door and he climbed in there.

Wonder what's going on 'ere, thought Toby. Must be checkin' in the back of the car to make sure he's got everything he needs till he comes back into Aramac, again.

Anyhow, old Jack kept fumbling about in the back of the car, searching here, there and everywhere. Then, when he looked up and saw Toby still standing on the step of the pub, old Jack reached over and opened the car door and he called out, 'Hey, Toby, I thought we said that these Aramac people were supposed'ta be honest. Well they're bloody well not, 'cause some bugger's gone 'n' pinched me bloody steerin' wheel.'

It's All to Do with Practice

(Shearing Stories)

The wife used to do the cooking for the shearers, see. For lunch and such she'd take the food down to the shed so they could have it there, then for tea they'd come on up to the house.

Anyhow, one day she decided to give the shearers a bit of a treat, so she made up a batch of cream puffs. Of course things like cream puffs weren't the normal food for the shearers. Cream puffs were well above what they usually ate, so, of course, they raved about it, one bloke in particular. For the sakes of the story we'll call him Ted.

'Beautiful,' Ted said as he demolished the last cream puff and licked his fingers, 'just beautiful.'

Anyway, when the shearers came back the following year, Ted was in the team again. Then, just as they were about to leave and head off to a new shed, Ted came up to the wife and he said, 'You never cooked any of them cream puffs this time, Missus.'

'Well,' the wife said, 'I would've loved to but the chooks have been off the lay and I never had any eggs.'

So the next year when the shearers came back, Ted brung along some eggs just to make sure that the wife could cook up some more of her cream puffs. And, you know, every time after that when Ted arrived with the shearing team, and we're talking something like over a period of fifteen years, the first thing he did was to come over to the house. 'Here Missus,' he'd say, and hand over a stack of eggs so that she could make up a big batch of cream puffs.

And it was the same shearer feller, Ted, who was the one with the great sense of humour. Given half a chance he'd string anyone along. He'd put it over you too, if he could, which was something he did quite often.

But, anyhow, this one particular season I had a new young roustabout in the shed. Very keen he was. Not too bright, mind you, but very keen. I forget his name now but he was a weedy sort of kid, needed a lot of strengthening up. Anyway, Ted started leading this young feller along something terrible. Every chance he had, Ted'd dish out the compliments and tell the kid that if he practised a bit more he'd soon become the strongest bloke around.

Of course the kid lapped it up and, what's more, he began believing it. Like during morning smoko Ted'd say, 'Sonny, bet yer can't do fifty push-ups.' Then the young roustie would hit the floor in a flash and huff and puff and go on until he'd done fifty push-ups.

'Well,' Ted'd say, looking astounded at the feat, 'that was great, son. I reckon with a bit of practice yer'd soon be the strongest bloke around.'

And you'd just about see the young feller's chest puff up with pride. Then any chance he got you'd see him, he'd be down on the floor practising his push-ups. Then during afternoon smoko Ted'd say something like, 'Sonny, bet yer can't do fifty chin-ups.' And the kid'd jump up, find a place, and do his fifty chin-ups.

'Well, that was great, son,' Ted'd say. 'I reckon with a bit of practice yer'd soon be the strongest bloke around.'

And again you'd just about see the young feller's chest expand. Then any chance he got you'd see him, he'd find a place and he'd be practising his chin-ups.

Now this went on right through the shearing with Ted winding this kid up and you just knew that it was all leading somewhere. But the young roustie took the bait every time. And still Ted kept boosting him up. 'Hey, sonny,' he'd call, 'yer a lot stronger than me, how's about yer get in the pen there and grab that ram and drag him over here fer me.'

And the kid'd be in that pen like lightning and grab the ram and huff and puff and eventually drag him over to the stand.

'Thanks son, that was great,' Ted'd say. 'I tell yer, with a bit of practice yer'd soon be the strongest bloke around.'

So, by the time shearing season was drawing to a close, Ted had this young roustie eating out of the palm of his hand. He'd completely buttered him up. Anything Ted asked, the young roustie would do it and when he'd done it he was showered with compliments and told that, with a bit of practice, he'd soon be the strongest bloke around.

Then on the last day of shearing, Ted said to the roustie, 'You know, son,' he said, 'I've seen some bloody strong blokes in me time and, by the living Harry, I reckon yer getting to be as strong as the best of them.' And you could see that the kid was over the moon with the compliment. Then Ted said, 'Look, how's about we see just how strong yer really are?'

'Okay,' said the young roustie, eager and ready to prove himself yet again.

'Well,' Ted said, 'I knew a bloke once who was so strong that he could stand in half a kerosene tin, grab hold of the handles, and lift himself completely offa the ground.'

'Gimme a go,' said the kid, not even realising the trick.

So Ted got out a half kerosene tin which still had the bottom in it. Back then we used to cut them in half and stick a couple of wire handles in the tops so that we could carry water around in them. Anyway, this tin, it would've been about eighteen inches by eighteen inches by about two feet high, open at the top and, like I said, still with its bottom in for carrying water. And that was where the trick lay. How could you lift yourself off the ground if you were standing in the tin, which still had the bottom in it? But the kid didn't even twig. He'd been buttered up so much by Ted that he was willing to try anything to prove his strength.

Anyway, to the great amusement of everyone in the shed, this kid stood in the half kerosene tin and he grabbed hold of the handles and he started trying to lift himself off the ground. Well he pulled and he grunted and he pulled and he groaned and he pulled some more. Just about busted his boiler he did, trying to lift himself off the ground.

Then eventually Ted stepped in. 'Bad luck, son. Yer nearly did it,' he said with a wink to his mates. 'But yer know what, young feller,' he added, 'I reckon with a bit of practice that by next season yer might just be able to lift yerself right off the ground.'

'Yeah, I reckon I might too,' the eager young roustie replied. 'It's all to do with practice, eh, Ted.'

Emergency!

(More Flying Doctor Stories)

Just a quick story and you may have already heard it. It's not my story. It was told by a well-known doctor-surgeon who used to be here in Dubbo, in central New South Wales. The doctor's name was Bob North. I think that's what his name was, anyway. Anyhow, Bob told this one at his farewell presentation, type of thing, about four years ago, when he was leaving or retiring or whatever he was doing.

Bob reckoned he was on duty in at Dubbo Hospital, one time, and there was this other doctor, a much younger feller, who'd just arrived from Sydney. I'd say he'd only been in Dubbo for a very short time. As far as I know he was straight out of university. The thing is, he was new at the job so he was pretty inexperienced as far as the more practical matters of doctoring go.

Anyhow, Bob was working flat out in surgery, performing some extremely delicate operation. It was something very critical so he was very focused and very busy and this young doctor comes racing into the surgery. 'There's an emergency,' he says. 'We've just taken a telephone call from the Flying Doctor base and they want a doctor to fly up to Lightning Ridge with them, immediately.'

'What's the problem?' Bob asked while still focusing on the job at hand.

'Well, they say that there's a bloke up there who's fallen down one of the mine shafts.'

'Doesn't sound too good,' Bob replied.

'No,' said the young doctor, 'apparently he's been stuck down the mine shaft for about a week, with nothing to eat, and he's only been keeping himself alive by drinking his own urine.'

Anyway, Bob said, 'Well, son, as you can see, I'm flat out, so you'll have to go up to Lightning Ridge with the RFDS by yourself and see to the feller.'

Of course, this really threw the new doctor into a flap. Being just out of university this was something very different than what he'd ever been taught.

'Well,' the young doctor said, looking to Bob for some wise and worldly advice, 'what do I do when I get there? How do I go about treating him? What's the procedure?'

'Well, son,' Bob said, still concentrating on his patient, 'the first thing yer gonna have to try and do is to get the feller off the piss.'

Next to Buckley's

(More Flying Doctor Stories)

This happened many years ago, when I was working up bush, at the Moomba gas and oil fields. Moomba's in the far north-east of South Australia so it's usually a desolate, dry country, as you might be able to imagine. But at this particular time there'd been a lot of rain and it'd caused flooding all through the north-east, and there was this guy who'd always dreamed of doing a walking trek from Innamincka, north-west through the Sturt Stony Desert and up to Birdsville, which is just over the border into Queensland. He was a very experienced bushman and he'd done all his research and all that sort of stuff, so he was well prepared. Then he decided to take a younger mate along with him, an English feller, who was a very inexperienced bushman. So they decided to do this walk.

Now, it was the middle of winter and by then the weather was okay: bitterly cold at night, mind you, but the days were okay, and not too hot. As I said the experienced bushman had done his homework, right. They had a radio with them, plus all the maps and they had backpacks and a cart to carry their supplies. They'd even organised rendezvous points along the way, where they'd meet people and pick up fresh supplies.

So they set off from Innamincka and they'd been walking for a couple of days. But what happens up in those regions is that, when you get big rains, a lot of water comes down all the little creeks and what-have-you, and they overflow and then you get these huge floodplain areas — like surface water spreading out everywhere. Now all this surface water doesn't appear on a map because it's rarely there. So they were walking along and they came to this big lake, over a floodplain, which wasn't on the map. They then had to make a decision: what do we do? Do we take a couple of extra days to go around it or do we try and wade across?

As a trial, they walked out a couple of hundred yards and it was only, you know, a foot deep or something like that. 'Well, it can't be too deep,' they said, and they decided to walk across this lake.

But there must've been a washaway or a creek that they didn't know about or wasn't on the map, right? So they were wading along, carrying all their gear — the experienced feller was strapped to the supply-cart — and suddenly they went from water that was about a foot deep to water that was right over their heads. They both went under and because they had lots of gear strapped onto them, they sunk like rocks.

Now, somehow the inexperienced Englishman managed to struggle to the surface. Then, when he got to safety he realised that his mate, the experienced bushman, wasn't there. So he went looking for him and some time later he found him, but unfortunately he'd drowned.

Anyhow, the Englishman's first thought was, 'I'd better get this guy back to the shore.'

So he unstrapped all of the dead feller's gear, and he left his own gear there and he started dragging his dead mate all the way back through this stretch of water. Eventually, he got the body to dry ground but then, when he went back to retrieve his gear, it was gone. Everything. He couldn't find it. So there he was, trapped out in the middle of nowhere, with nothing but the clothes he's wearing, which were, basically, just a pair of shorts and a T-shirt. That's all. He'd even taken his shoes off to swim. So now he's thinking, 'Well, what do I do now? How do I get myself out of this mess? I've never been in the outback before. I don't know how to navigate. I don't even know where I am. I don't have any maps. Nothing. I'm going to die.'

Then he remembered that two days previously they'd crossed something that resembled a road, so he thought, 'If I can get back to the road I might be able to find someone or track someone down.'

Obviously, he couldn't take his dead mate with him so he had to leave the body there and he starts backtracking. There's plenty of water because there's lots of waterholes, you know, but he hasn't got any food. Not a crumb. Nothing. So for two days he walks back the way they'd come and eventually he stumbles across this road, right. But, unbeknown to the Englishman, the road wasn't a real road, it was what's known as a shot line, okay? Now, what a shot line is: with oil and gas mining they sort of bulldoze these tracks like grid lines so that when they fly over them, they can use them for survey lines, you see? Vehicles don't drive up and down them, they're basically put in and abandoned, right? But this guy thought it was a road. But it's not — it's a shot line.

So he thinks, 'Good, I've got to this road but now, what do I do? Do I sit here and wait for a car to come along or do I keep moving?'

Well, he sat and waited for a while and there was no sight of a car so he decides it'd be better to keep moving. But then he was faced with another problem: do I turn right and walk and see what I can find or do I turn left and walk and see what I find?

Now, what you've got to realise, this's out in the Sturt Stony Desert and the nearest town is Innamincka, and that's like 100 kilometres away. What's more, the guy's got no idea where he is; not even a clue. But he decides, for whatever reason, he doesn't really know: I'll turn left and walk down the road a bit and see how I go.

So he turns left and starts walking down this shot line, which really isn't a road. Then about 100 yards further on he walks over a rise and sitting there, in the middle of all this nowhere, is a wrecked telephone booth.

Now, what had happened was, about fifteen years before the Englishman arrived on the spot, there'd been a little camp there that they'd used when they were grading the shot lines, and maybe drilling a couple of holes or something like that. So years ago there'd been a small camp there, you know, with five or ten guys, living in caravans for about four or five weeks before they moved on. And back then, what sometimes happened was that, with these little camps, they never used radios for communication. They only had one of those old wind-up telephones, right, and they'd just plonk it in the middle of a camp, stick a bit of a telephone box around it and they'd run maybe 20 or 30 miles of telephone cable, above ground and, when they happened to come across another telephone cable, they'd just cut into that, alright. Then, when they abandoned the camp, they'd pick up the telephone box, wind the cable up and move on to the next site and set it all up again. But for some inexplicable reason, on this one and only occasion, they'd up and left and they'd abandoned this telephone and the wires.

So, you know, this guy sees this telephone box like it's an apparition. But it's been exposed to the elements for donkey's ages; the doors are hanging off, there's no windows, the old Bakelite receiver's all cracked, wires are hanging off it and, you know, there's a dirt floor. So the Englishman thinks, 'Well, in for a penny, in for a pound.' And he jumps into this telephone box, picks up the receiver, he winds the handle and, all of a sudden, out of the deadness comes this voice. 'Hello Santos, Moomba Coms, can I help you?'

Now, for some strange reason this telephone box was not only still there but it'd never been disconnected, as well. And this guy just couldn't believe his luck, right? He's out in the middle of nowhere and finds a telephone box and an old wind-up receiver and he gets straight through to Santos Communications at Moomba. So the Englishman told his tale of woe to the communications guy. Then the Coms guy said, 'Look, okay, but do you have any idea where you are because we can't track you on this telephone line. We didn't even know it existed.'

'I've got no idea,' the Englishman said. But he tried giving him a basic outline, you know, like, 'We were walking between Innamincka and Birdsville and then two days later this accident happened and I backtracked for a couple of days and I came across this road and I turned left and I think I headed south, but I'm not quite sure.'

So the guy at Moomba said, 'Alright, well, tell you what, stay on the line, I've got a couple of old blokes who were out on the surveying camps years ago. They might remember the area so perhaps they can give us a rough idea of, maybe, where you might be.'

In actual fact the Coms guy didn't hold out much hope. But anyway, he rings up a couple of old blokes and they come in and get the story. They don't hold out too much hope either but they get out their old surveying maps — the ones they'd had stored away at the back of their wardrobes for the past twenty years or so — and they blow the dust off them and lay them out on the table. So there's these two old crusty miners, you know, looking at these maps and going like, 'Gawd, it could be this camp.' 'No it couldn't be that one but I remember this camp. That could be the one.' And between them they, sort of, figured out, 'Well, he might be somewhere in this region here but, you know, then he could be somewhere else. But if we were going to have a stab in the dark, here's as good a place as any to start looking.'

And that's when they got the Flying Doctor Service involved. As I said, I was working up there at the time. So they called me over and they said, 'Well, look, we've got a guy. He's out bush somewhere and he's found an old telephone and he's on the line and we're going to try and find him.'

So we got the helicopter pilot in for a briefing and these crusty old miners said, 'I reckon we should do a grid search, starting from here and just see how we go.'

'That's fine by me,' the chopper pilot said. 'We'll start at that point and just work our way back in a criss-cross pattern.'

And well, what you've got to realise is that the lost Englishman could've been at any one of about a hundred and fifty possible old camp sites, okay? Anyway, off we all go in the chopper and this Englishman's still on the phone talking to Moomba Coms and he looks out of the broken down old telephone box and he sees this helicopter away in the distance, and we could see the phone box and we could see him waving and we're thinking, 'Oh God, this is unbelievable. It's a miracle. We've found him.'

Now, from him making the telephone call to us finding him would've only taken, probably, an hour. Mind you, he'd already been wandering around out there for a couple of days without adequate clothing and, of course, no food. But as luck would have it, that was the first point in our search pattern. So we landed the chopper and the pilot, he switches the engine off and he walks over to this English guy, who's still standing there with the phone in his hand, wondering if what he's seeing is really real or not, and the pilot says to him, 'Excuse me, were you the guy who phoned for a taxi?'

And this guy couldn't believe it. Well, neither could we. All the cards had fallen his way. He told me later that he thought it was sort of a religious experience. Like, I know his mate died and all that sort of stuff but he said, 'I've never believed in God but gees, I do now because, you know, there I was out in the desert with next to Buckley's of getting found and all of a sudden an ancient telephone box appears that somehow gets me through to Moomba Coms and then a helicopter arrives out of nowhere to pick me up.'

Anyway, before we went back and retrieved his mate's body we flew the Englishman back to Moomba and, amazingly, he wasn't too badly exposed. His feet were really blistered and he had a bit of sunburn. But, you know, in the scheme of things, he wasn't too bad, though he did keep saying how hungry he was, which you could understand. So when we arrived back at Moomba, of course, all his clothes were shredded and as we walked into the Health Centre I threw him a pair of overalls and said, 'Look mate, just put these on and we'll go and get you something to eat.'

And he went, 'Oh great because, like, I'm really hungry, you know.'

Well, he threw the overalls on and I took him over to the Moomba mess hall. Now, the Moomba mess hall is this great big, gigantic dining room, which can cater for about four hundred workers, right, and the food's phenomenal. You can get just about anything. You know, this is around lunchtime and there's salads and sandwiches and four different sorts of hot meals and there's an ice-cream machine there, and desserts. It's like a huge buffet at a hotel. So we go into this mess room and this guy, well, here he is, an hour and a half earlier he thought he was going to die from starvation and now he walks into this food fest.

'Can I have anything I want?' he said.

I said, 'Go for it mate, you're the one that hasn't eaten for days.'

So he grabbed a plate and he piled it full of T-bone steaks, right. And I've never seen a guy go through three T-bone steaks so quick in my life. He just wolfed them down. And he'd just finished this enormous meal, right, and he turned to me and he said, 'Oh, cripes, I've just forgotten. I'm a vegetarian. I haven't eaten meat in ten years.' Then he added, 'But I tell you what, that was the best meal I've ever had in my life.'

Railway Folklore

(Railway Stories)

I've got a few little stories here. I don't know if you can use them or not but they're sort of a part of railway folklore, so I'm sure they'd make for some fun reading whatever the case.

The first one's about a country lad who came to Sydney to find work. The only trouble was that he wasn't trained for much outside of farming so he decided his best bet was to do a course in travel guide hosting, which he did. Anyhow, on his first day out around the sights of Sydney he was given the job as a guide to a busload of foreign tourists.

First they set out to see the Sydney Harbour Bridge. The young lad, now full of knowledge, proudly stood up and announced to the tourists, 'We are now passing the Sydney Harbour Bridge, colloquially known as the "Coathanger" because of its distinctive shape and design.' Then he went on to tell everyone what year it was built, when it was opened, how long it took to build and all the other relevant details. When he finished talking he sat down feeling quite pleased with his efforts — that was, until there came a loud voice from down the back of the bus, 'Oh, in mar country we would'a built that there bridge ten times larger and in half that time.'

Being mild of manner the lad let the comment be, and next they moved on to the Opera House, where he began his spiel again. 'We are passing the Sydney Opera House, colloquially known as the "Sails" because of its distinctive shape and design.' Then he went on to tell everyone what year it was built, when it was opened, how long it took to build and all the other relevant details. Then just as he'd sat down there came the same loud voice from down the back of the bus, 'Oh, in mar country we would'a built that there opera house ten times larger and in half that time.'

Anyhow, this proved to be the theme of the day. At every attraction they came across the lad would describe the sight, informing his passengers of what year the particular structure was built, when it was opened, how long it took to build and all the other relevant details. And countering his every word, the loud voice from the back of the bus kept repeating that, in his country it would've been built ten times larger and in half the time than it'd taken the Australians.

Towards the end of the tour they were coming back down George Street and they were just passing Central railway station when the same loud voice called out, 'Hey, feller, what's that large building over there?'

Well by this stage the young guide had had enough so he stood up and replied, 'Buggered if I know, mate. It wasn't there this morning.'

Another one in that same vein happened on the North Coast Daylight, going up through the Dungog area. Anyhow, there were a couple of middle-aged big mouths on the train who were going on and on in that extremely annoying way of theirs, about how everything from their country was bigger and better. Oh, they were driving everyone in the carriage crazy, absolutely crazy.

Anyhow, there wasn't a big buffet car on on this particular day. It was tray service and one of the young buffet girls or, to use their official name, 'Train Catering Service Staff', was serving lunch and one of the big mouths said to this youngster, 'Excuse me, mii-sss.'

'Yes, sir?' she said, in a very polite manner.

'Mii-sss,' he said, 'would there be any kaan-garr-oos around here?'

And that youngster, like a shot, she said, 'No, sir, but I know where there's a couple of silly old galahs.'

And these two big mouths couldn't work out why the whole carriage erupted into laughter. That girl almost got a standing ovation.

The next story's about two strangers — a man and a woman — who boarded the Indian Pacific in Adelaide to travel over to Perth. As it turned out, the train was overcrowded and their bookings got mixed up and these two strangers ended up having to share a sleeping berth. Anyhow, as they were crossing the Nullarbor the temperature dropped and the female, who was on the top bunk, asked the male on the bottom bunk, 'Could you please pass me up a blanket, it's cold up here.'

Upon hearing this request, the man in the bottom bunk said, 'I've only got one blanket and I'm using it myself so, no, you can't have it.' Anyhow, the woman in the top bunk came up with a suggestion. 'Well then,' she said, 'how about we pretend we're married and then we can share the blanket?' To which the reply from the male was, 'What do you mean by "we pretend we're married"?'

'Exactly what I said,' replied the woman.

'Okay then,' the bloke said, 'if that's the case, get yer own bloody blanket.'

Another one's about an old man sitting on a railway bench at Caboolture, just north of Brisbane. He was waiting for his train to arrive when along came a young lad with his hair all spiked up in all different colours and he sat down beside the old man. Anyhow, the old chap kept looking at this lad, long and hard. Then after a while, this constant staring got to the young lad so he said, 'Hey, old man, haven't yer ever done nothin' wild 'n' radical in yer life?'

'Oh yes,' replied the old man. 'Years ago,' he said, 'I was out west, out past Longreach, and I got lost in the scrub for months and I got so lonely and frustrated that I ended up having sex with a western lorikeet.'

'Yeah, 'n' so what?' said the young man.

'Well,' said the old feller, 'I'm just now wondering if you might be me son.'

Then the last one's about a train driver. Now, quite often, train drivers have a reputation for being grumpy and this feller was no exception. Just to give you an example, before I go into my story, there's an old railway friend of mine who used to pen some poems and he wrote this one:

> *The guard is a man who sits in the van, in the van at the*
> *back of the train.*
> *The driver up front*
> *thinks the guard is a so-and-so*
> *and the guard thinks the driver's the same.*

So that'll give you some idea as to the grumpiness of some of these drivers. Anyway, there he was, this engine driver, down in the Hobart shunting yards, sitting in the loco, waiting for his usual fireman to arrive. Anyhow, his fireman's running extremely late, which puts the driver in an even grumpier mood than he's usually in. Then along hurries a young man who jumps up in the cabin and says to the driver, 'I'm yer fireman for the day. Ben's got the flu.'

Well the train driver looks down his nose at this young fireman and he grunts, 'So what's yer name?'

'Charlie, sir.'

'I don't address my firemen by their Christian names, son,' the driver snapped. 'Give me your surname.'

'Darling, sir,' comes the reply from the fireman.

'Okay then, Charlie, start shovelling,' grunted the driver.

Shovlin' Shit

(Railway Stories)

Back around the late 1940s, early '50s, I knew a bloke who was a train drover. Now this train drover worked out of bush stockyards throughout the Riverina and Victoria, and it was his responsibility to look after trainloads of stock — mainly sheep — until they'd reached the meatworks near Melbourne. Like, if any of the sheep fell over during transit he'd get them back on their feet again so that they wouldn't get injured or die. Then when the train reached the meatworks he'd supervise the unloading of the sheep before jumping on the next train back bush to repeat the process.

After the train had been unloaded, as you might imagine, the stock trucks would be pretty soiled, with having carried all these sheep. So what the railways did was, they employed someone to 'muck out' the trucks. To put it simply, the job entailed shovlin' the sheep manure out of the stock trucks before giving them a squirt down with a hose so they'd be ready to head back bush for another load, and you'd do that day after day after day.

Now the particular bloke that my train drover mate knew who did this mucking out was a feller called George, and this George was pretty new to the job — what's more, he was a little bit below par as far as intelligence went. I won't draw any conclusions there other than to say, it was the only job he could get with the qualifications he had.

Anyhow, so they could get paid each week, all Victorian railway employees had to fill out a work-report form and on that form they had to write a brief description of the activity they'd undertaken and the number of hours they'd worked at that activity. Then after they'd filled out the form they'd hand it into the accountant who'd check it over then send it into the pay office in Spencer Street, where it'd be processed. So when George filled in his work-report he'd write:

Monday — shovlin' sheep shit — 8 hours.
Tuesday — shovlin' sheep shit — 8 hours.
Wednesday — shovlin' sheep shit — 8 hours.

And so on until he reached Friday.

Now, as my mate told it, the accountant got wind that the pay ladies at the head office, in Spencer Street, were feeling a little uncomfortable with George's continued use of the word 'shit'. It just wasn't done in those days. So the railway's accountant got George into his office to explain the situation. George arrived, fresh from the railway yards, smelling to high heaven. 'Look, George,' the accountant said, 'the ladies in the pay office are a bit disturbed with the use of the word "shit" on your work-report form, so how about you start writing the word "excrement" instead.'

And George said, 'Christ almighty, mate, if I knew how to spell the word "excrement" I wouldn't be stuck out there shovlin' shit, would I?'

Gymkhanas

(New Flying Doctor Stories)

My name's John Lynch. I'm the CEO of the Royal Flying Doctor Service's Central Operations and, if you've got a minute, I've got a few stories to tell. Now, due to the isolation of the outback, the local gymkhanas are a huge social occasion for station people and the like who otherwise would rarely have the chance to get together. And of course, while everyone's in the one place, we usually set up a tent to run a medical clinic so that people can have a health check or whatever. Now I'm particularly talking about the blokes here because, you know, while they're all in town for the gymkhana, it's an opportune time to grab them where there's less focus on them having to make a special appointment and come all the way into town to visit the doctor. You know what blokes are like.

So it'll quite often be, 'Well, mate, if you go across to see the doctor for a health check, I may as well go too.'

'Okay then, let's all go.' That sort of thing.

And also the gymkhanas are usually designed as a fundraiser for the Royal Flying Doctor Service. So I've got a few stories about gymkhanas, and I guess that the first of these stories goes to demonstrate the huge excitement that a gymkhana generates. Now, we had a new doctor who'd never been to a gymkhana and, as I said before, a gymkhana is one of those rare opportunities when everyone gets together. What's more, you must appreciate that some of these young, single fellers and girls might never have had a lot of regular social contact, particularly with the opposite sex. So when they get together they sometimes get pretty — how can I say it? — 'frisky'.

Anyway, one of our new doctors went up to this town to run the on-course medical clinic. He arrived on the morning of the gymkhana and the first thing he did was that he went over to the nursing station to introduce himself. 'Hello,' he said, 'I'm Dr so-and-so from the Flying Doctor Service.'

'Yep, no worries,' said the nurse. They all knew his name.

'Oh, I almost forgot,' said the doctor, and he handed over a package to the nurse. 'There you go; I brought along some condoms, just in case they're needed.'

And the nurse looked at him and she said, 'I reckon you might be a bit too late, doctor. The mob got into town last night and they've been having a hell of a good time ever since.'

So the party had already begun.

Then, after he handed over the condoms, this new doctor went off and he set up a little tent to do his medical checks and some of these younger kids, of course they run around all day and they have busters and so forth and so they're always going to the doctor to get their grazes fixed up. Anyhow, one young kid arrives with a grazed knee and the doctor's taking a look at it when a call comes over the loudspeaker: 'Could the Flying Doctor come urgently to the finishing post.'

Instantly of course he thinks, 'Dear me, someone's fallen off a horse and injured themselves badly.'

So the doctor tried to hurry up with this kid but he's interrupted by another call over the loudspeaker: 'The Flying Doctor is very urgently required at the finishing post.'

'Look,' the doctor said to the kid, 'there's an emergency so I'll just stick a band-aid over your graze and if it's still bothering you, come back later and I'll sort it out properly.'

Then he quickly stuck a band-aid on the kid, grabbed his medical bag and he took off like a rocket, out of the tent, through the crowd, under the fence, out onto the track and over to the finishing post, all the while preparing himself for the worst. Then, when he got to the finishing post, he ran up to the bloke with the microphone and he said, 'Yes ... (puff) ... yes ... I'm ... (puff) ... the Flying Doctor. Where's the emergency?'

And the bloke on the microphone said, 'Where the hell have you been? We've been waiting for you to come and draw the bloody raffle.'

So I guess that goes to show the social intricacies of a gymkhana, and what the responsibilities and the expectations sometimes are of the people from the Flying Doctor Service. And we're ever so lucky that those outback people are also just fundamentally open and honest with you. In many ways it's as if we're one big family. It's like that old bloke in one of the original promotional videos, or was it a film? But anyway, I saw this footage of an old weather-beaten bush character. He's right out in the outback and, you know, he's got the typical old battered hat — pushed back with sweat stains all around the brim — that'd been worn for that many years it'd become part of the personality. And even though you don't see it much today because of the health risks, he's got the roll-your-own cigarette, hanging out the side of his mouth, he's wearing the standard checked shirt, with a tin of tobacco stuck in the top pocket, sleeves rolled up, the RM Williams riding boots and the well-worn jeans, and they asked him, 'What does the Flying Doctor mean to you?'

And the old feller, he said, 'The Flying Doctor?' Then he pushed back his hat and scratched his forehead, while he had a bit of a think. Then, with just the slightest glint in his eye, he answered, 'Well,' he said, 'without the Royal Flying Doctor Service I'd reckon there'd be a hell of a lotta dead people livin' out here.'

And, again, that's just so typical of those people. Wonderful people. Wonderful humour.

But while we're talking about gymkhanas and wonderful fellers with wonderful humour, I must mention Johnny Watkins, 'Watto' as he's known. Watto just happens to have found the recipe for that weather-beaten outback look. He's a terrific feller and just one of the greatest supporters of the RFDS. In fact, he's a wonderful supporter of the bush. Watto was the Elders man and auctioneer throughout the north of South Australia so naturally he landed the job as the auctioneer at the William Creek Gymkhana, which is another great fundraising event for the RFDS. It was my first time up at William Creek and a lot of people from Port Augusta got together and formed a syndicate to buy horses for the day in an attempt to try and win some cup or ribbon or other. Of course, much of the money from the buying of horses goes to the Flying Doctor Service.

Anyway, being the CEO of the RFDS in that area, I thought that maybe I should buy a horse as well. Well, the truth be known, Watto very strongly suggested that I should buy a horse. Now I didn't have a clue about horses but Watto stepped in and he told me, in the strictest of confidences, that the next horse to be auctioned was a 'real beauty'. Apparently it had some sort of 'impeccable breeding'. Even the name Bart Cummings may have been mentioned. I forget now but Watto described it as being the 'sleeper' of the entire gymkhana.

'Okay,' I said, 'I'll bid for it.'

'Don't worry,' said Watto, 'I'll make sure you get it at a reasonable price.'

So the bidding begins and Watto calls out, 'Who can start me off with $20?'

Well, I stick my hand up to put in my bid, fully expecting to get the horse for twenty dollars; it sounded like a bargain to me, even being a mug punter. But then Watto said, 'I've got $30. Who can better $30 for this beautifully bred horse? Yes, $40 ... $50 ... Yes, $60 to Johnny Lynch the CEO. $70 ... $80 ... $120 to Johnny Lynch.' And I'm just standing there. I haven't even moved a muscle. I only bid $20 on this nag and the next thing Watto's telling me that I've just bid $120 for it.

Anyway, I finally end up getting this 'beautifully bred horse' — this dead cert — for something like $150 and the only thing I'm dead certain about is that I was the only one to have put in a single bid. No one else even bothered. But anyway, I've got this horse, so I said to Watto, 'What do I do now?'

And he said, 'You need to go over and pay for it.'

So I started to walk across to where I had to pay for the horse and this young feller come up and he said, 'You got a jockey, Boss?'

I said, 'A jockey? No.' I hadn't even thought about a jockey.

'Well,' he said, 'who's ridin' the horse?'

I said, 'I don't know.'

'I'm a jockey,' he said. 'I'm the best.'

'Oh, are you?' I said.

He said, 'You want me to be your jockey?'

I said, 'Well, okay, then.' I said, 'If you want to be my jockey, then you've got the job.'

'Yeah, Boss,' he said, 'I'm the best. You won't regret it.' Then he said, 'Well, we'd better put the horse in the race.'

'Yeah, no worries,' I said. 'What race will we go in?'

He said, 'All of 'em.'

And so the relationship had been struck, and this young feller made it clear that because I was the owner of the horse, I was to be known as the 'Boss', and he was to be called the 'Boy', as, apparently that's what jockeys are called by the owners. And he rode that horse — that dead cert — in every event that was on. There was the peg race. Then they had the distance race. Then there was a 400-metre race. Then there was some bloody race where the horse went around and around in ever decreasing circles. And we never got a prize; never even got a ribbon. Not even a placing. Nothing. In fact, there was one race where the jockey — the 'Boy' — had to go and pick up pegs then put them into a barrel, and I said to him after the race, 'If they have that race again,' I said, 'is there any chance that the horse can ride you because the horse is too bloody slow and you keep missing the barrel.'

But, you know, he was a terrific little feller. I think he said he was nineteen, and he rode in every race. And he never missed me because after each disastrous event he always came across to explain to me what had gone wrong with the horse. Then I'd thank him for the explanation and I'd pay him a couple of bob for the ride.

'Thanks, Boss,' he'd say. 'We'll have better luck next time.'

But we never did.

In the ...

(New Flying Doctor Stories)

When I first went up to Cape York to work with the Australian Inland Mission, there was a story going around that went something like this. Now, you know how cooks have the reputation of being temperamental people. Well, one of the station properties had this rather large cook who, when he got into a 'paddy' about anything, would grab a book and go out and plonk himself down in the outhouse toilet and, depending on the gravity of the paddy he was in, maybe not come out for anything up to a couple of hours.

Of course, back then there weren't any septic systems in those remote areas so the type of toilets they used were the 'long-drop' type. For those of you that may not know, the long-drop toilet is basically, you know, a wooden box type of thing with a hole in the top where the seat goes, and that's all placed over a very deep hole, which is where all the 'waste' goes. For privacy, it's surrounded by a few sheets of corrugated iron, a roof and a wooden door. That particular style of toilet was well suited to Cape York because, being an old mining area, the actual toilet itself was simply plonked down over an old mine shaft, which saved a lot of digging.

Anyway, early one morning this cranky cook got his knickers in a knot about something or other, so he grabbed a book and went out and plonked himself down on the toilet. Unfortunately, the white ants must've been very busy of late because when he sat down the toilet crumbled from under him and he, in turn, disappeared down this old mine shaft. Actually, you could liken it to what happened to Alice in the book *Alice in Wonderland*, except that this cook really landed in the ... well, you can imagine what he landed in, can't you?

Now, seeing that all the ringers and stockmen and that who worked on this station property were well aware of the cook's temperamental nature, when he hadn't come out of the toilet by breakfast time they didn't worry too much, and they just went ahead and helped themselves. Even by morning tea there was still only some semi-mild concern. But by lunchtime, some hours later, these stockmen were starting to get pretty hungry and even though the cook wasn't what you'd call 'a gourmet specialist', at least he dished up a pretty hearty meal.

Anyway, one of the younger ringers drew the short straw and he got landed with the job of going over to the outhouse to check on the situation. So he wandered over to the long-drop, knocked on the wooden door and said, 'Cookie, are yer okay?'

There was no answer so the ringer knocked a little louder, 'Hey, Cookie, we're getting hungry.'

Still no answer. Then, just as the ringer was about to walk away, he thought he heard a very faint voice. 'This's a bit odd,' thought the ringer and he called out for his mates to come over and offer a second opinion. They all gathered around the outhouse. 'Hey, Cookie!' they shouted.

'Help,' came the distant reply.

So they broke down the toilet door and that's when they discovered that the cook had disappeared down the old mine shaft.

'Hey, Cookie, are yer down there?'

'Yes,' came the echo.

Anyway, while someone went over to the homestead to get on the radio and call the Flying Doctor, the stockmen knocked down the outer, corrugated iron, toilet structure and then they got the ropes and all the rest of it and they hooked up a 'windlass' — a winch lift — to haul the cook out.

Even though the cook had been extricated from his predicament by the time the Flying Doctor arrived, the poor chap was still in rather a smelly state. But the doctor, being the professional that he was, checked the cook out to make sure that he was okay and luckily, apart from a very bruised ego, the cook had survived the experience without too many injuries at all. But just to be on the safe side, the doctor decided to give him a course of antibiotics, because of the, you know, the particular situation he'd been in. And as the story went, the cook lost a little of his temperamental sharpness after that event and even when he did throw a paddy, just before he'd storm out of the kitchen he'd announce to all and sundry, 'Won't be long, fellers.'

The Ghost Who Talks

(Bush Funeral Stories)

Inland from the central coast of New South Wales, there's a place called Gloucester. It's situated on the eastern side of the Great Dividing Range, right at the bottom of the Barrington Tops. So that's where it is — Gloucester.

Now, in their day, funeral directors were known as undertakers and working out of Gloucester was one of the real old-time bush undertakers, a feller that everyone simply called WT. I've been told that old WT started his business way back in the early 1920s. So it was a long time ago. That said, this incident happened later on, in the mid-to late '50s, when WT was nearing retirement and, with his want of keeping the business in the family, both WT's boys, Jed and Jeremiah, had started to work with him.

Anyhow, if they ever had to transfer the body of a deceased person down to Sydney for a burial, to save on expensive rail freight costs, WT would bring back an empty coffin or two in his hearse. On this occasion, when WT took a body down to Sydney, he'd taken his two boys with him, just to give them a taste of the big smoke. After they'd dropped off the coffin, containing the body of the deceased, they drove out to the Surry Hills warehouse and placed two empty coffins in the back of the hearse, head to toe. Then they headed back to Gloucester.

As I said, old WT was getting on a bit by this stage and, by then, driving long distances was quite tiring for him. So when they got to Newcastle, he pulled over the hearse.

'I'm done,' he said. 'One of you boys can take over the driving. I'm going to get in the back and have a lie down.'

'Okay, Dad,' said one of his sons — I think it might've been Jed, the eldest boy — 'I'll take over from here.'

'Thanks, son,' and so WT went around to the back of the hearse, opened the doors, took the lid off one of the coffins and he got in and laid down and dropped off to sleep.

After they'd got to Raymond Terrace, they had to branch off the Pacific Highway, and get onto the Bucketts Way, to head home via the small township of Stroud. By now it's just on dark. But that's okay because, while the headlights of the hearse had dulled over the years, it was one of those really bright, fluky sort of full moons — some might say 'eerie'. Anyhow, it would've taken them, say, half an hour to get to Stroud. Then, with the road between Stroud and Gloucester being akin to a knot of twists and curves, it usually took another three quarters of an hour to get home. I say 'usually' because you could add on an extra half an hour if you were held up at the railway gates, just outside of Stroud, by the Northern Mail, as it passed through on its way back down south.

And that's what happened. Just as they were arriving at the railway crossing, the gateman was shutting the gates. Now, for those that may not know, back in those days, they didn't have automatic warning lights at most bush railway crossings. Instead, New South Wales Railways employed a 'gateman'. And a gateman was a feller who lived in a small house, right next to the railway crossing, and, whenever a train was due to pass through, it was his job to go out and shut the gates to hold back the traffic. Then, after the train had passed, he'd open the gates again and everyone would be free to continue along their merry way.

Now the gateman at this particular crossing, the one just out of Stroud, was a feller called Bert Oldfield — no relation to the cricketer — and old WT had recently buried Bert's wife, Mavis. In doing so, Bert had got to know old WT and the boys quite well. So when Bert saw the hearse pull up with the two boys, Jed and Jeremiah, sitting in the front, to kill a bit of time until the Northern Mail had passed through, he wandered over to have a bit of a yarn.

'G'day, fellers,' Bert said. 'It's an odd sort'a full moonlit night, ay?'

'Too right,' said the sons in unison.

The thing was, just as the hearse had pulled up at the crossing, WT had woken from his slumber. And so, when he heard Bert's voice, he thought he may as well join in the conversation. So old WT sits up in the coffin, has a bit of a stretch, and he says through the flicker of the full moon, 'G'day, Bert. How's things?'

And that's the last they saw of Bert. They reckon that, even before the last of WT's words had left his lips, Bert had bolted. He was gone; off like a shot. So WT and his boys sat around for a while until the Northern Mail had passed through. Then they sat around for a while longer, waiting for Bert to come back and open the railway gates. Then, after a while longer, and with still no sign of Bert, Jed said, 'Hey, Dad, do you reckon it'd be okay if we open up the gates ourselves?'

'Sounds like a good idea, son,' said old WT.

So Jeremiah got out and opened the gates. Through they went and, as they wove their way homeward, along the Bucketts Way, Jed said, 'Gee, Dad, that Bert's a bit of a strange one, ay?'

The Normanton Bell

(Bush Priests Stories)

Dear Bill,

I came across your book New Great Australian Flying Doctor Stories *today and on seeing a story called 'The Normanton Bell' I read it first, as I lived in Normanton from 1955 to 1963, and knew Sam Henry and other characters mentioned. I knew the church well, and the bell, as a small group of us met there each week for a church service and I taught Sunday school there on the verandah, when it had been cleared of goat 'calling cards' and disinfected with carbolic (a lovely, lingering combination!).*

However, I wish to let you know that the padre you spoke about in the story did not work for the Presbyterian Australian Inland Mission. His name was Matthews and he and his wife were missionaries for the Aboriginal Inland Mission, founded by a Mrs Long in about 1907, and so predated John Flynn's well-known Australian Inland Mission by about twenty years. I knew the Matthews well and I became an associate worker for this mission for some of my years in Normanton. My husband was the first Powerhouse superintendent there.

Best wishes,

Daphne Hindmarsh

Well, that story was one I sort of also told you in my book *Goldie*, so, Swamp, we'd better get it right this time, for the lady, ay?

Any rate, this all happened back when I was up in the Gulf country — up in the north-west of Queensland, on the Gulf of Carpentaria. At the time of this story I was doing a bit of this, that and the other, including a bit of cattle duffing on the side. Right, so I'm back in Normanton and I'm out with the Caseys. The Caseys were big cattle duffers up that way, so I was staying with them. They owned a place called 'Shady Lagoons'. Any rate, I'd come into town from Shady Lagoons and I was drinking with a feller by the name of Jack McNab. Jack was a saddler and he also had a mail run. So me and him, we're up in the top pub — the National — and we'd been drinking on and off all the afternoon. Like, we're not downing them one after the other, we were just drinking nice and steady. Any rate by about 10 o'clock that night, Jack and me, we're starting to get a bit argumentative with each other and this argument's getting pretty warmed up. I forget what it was about just now, but it was heating up.

Just as things were getting pretty prickly between Jack and me, Sam Henry, the local sergeant, comes into the pub. So Sam Henry's sitting down the other end of the bar and he sees what's going on and he's thinking, Gees, it looks like a blue's on the cards here between Goldie and McNab. So Sam comes up and he goes through all the change we had on the counter and he hands it over to Ted Kershaw, the publican. 'Ted,' he says, 'give us a dozen beers.' In those days all the beer was in twenty-six-ounce bottles. The big ones. There was no stubbies.

So Ted goes and he gets the beer, see. 'Here yer go,' he says, and he hands it over to Sam Henry.

Then Sam says to me and Jack, 'Righto, youse fellers, come with me,' and he puts the carton on his shoulder and he walks out of the pub. So me and Jack, we follow him out. By now, me and Jack, we're just talking and going on. There's no arguing, we're just talking.

So then Sam gets into his vehicle. It's a ute sort of thing and Jack and me, we climb in the back and Sam drives us out to the edge of town, to an old timber church. Now this old church was built 'round the turn of the century, back in the early 1900s and at that stage it wasn't in very good nick. It'd weathered a lot of cyclones and so it's leaning over at about a thirty-degree angle. It was one of them old weatherboard ones that's up on stumps; you know, with the white ant caps on top. They didn't even hold church services there any more because there wasn't much floorboards left. Like, anybody in town who wanted a bit of timber always went down to the old church to get it. Yeah, that's where they went for their timber.

Any rate, Sam plonks us there, at this old church, with this dozen beers and he says, 'Righto, fellers, go fer yer life. Do what yer like,' then he jumps back in his car and he goes back into town.

Now, outside the front of the church, about thirty feet or something, there was still the original old bell and this old bell had a length of rope hanging off it. So me and Jack, we're left sitting there, ay? We'd both long forgot what the original argument was about so now we're bored and we're looking for something to do. Any rate, around Normanton there's a lot of goats walking around all the time so I says to Jack, I says, 'Let's have some fun. We'll catch a goat 'n tie its back leg ter the rope on the bell 'n as it's trying ter get away it'll be ringin' the bell.'

'Okay,' Jack says, and so we try to catch one of these goats, ay? But we're still a bit too drunk to catch a goat. They keep getting away from us.

'This's no good,' I says to Jack. 'We're gettin' nowhere so hows about we ring the bell ourselves?'

'Yeah,' Jack says. 'Good idea.'

So I starts ringing this bell, ay? By now it's about 2 o'clock in the morning and we're ringing away and we can see all these house lights being turned on around town, left, right and centre. Now, at that time, there was only one minister in Normanton. I forget his name just now but he was what they called a 'padre' because he belonged to — and I'll get it right this time — the Aboriginal Inland Mission. Any rate, he lived way over on the other side of Normanton. Way over. So I must've been making a real racket, ay, because next thing this padre comes flying down the road in his car.

I says, 'Oh, how yer goin', Padre? Have a drink.'

But he's in no mood for that, ay, because he heads off into this big lecture to me and Jack about the evils of drinking. Then he says, 'You shouldn't be ringing that bell.'

I says, 'Why's that?'

He says, 'Because when a church bell's rung, it's meant to be the call for all the sinners to come to church.'

So I says, 'Well, this must be a pretty righteous town ay, Padre?'

'Why's that?' he says.

I says, 'Because, Padre, you're the only person who's turned up.'

After that he sort of gave up on us, ay, and he got back in his car and he drove back into town. So that's the story of the Normanton bell and the Aboriginal Inland Mission padre, and I hope I got it right this time.

Fifteen Border Leicesters

(Trucking Stories)

Mate, I've got a truckies story or three here, but they're not real outback-outback ones, if you catch my drift. These are from around the Denny — Deniliquin — Finley, Tocumwal area in the southern Riverina region of New South Wales. This first one happened sometime back in the early '70s, when there was a hell of a lot of wheat around — so much so that the siloes were full to busting and we had to deliver the excess wheat to the aircraft hangers, out at the Tocumwal aerodrome. That's where they'd decided to store this overload of wheat.

Now, the procedure was, after you'd loaded your truck with the harvested wheat from out on the farm, you'd take it out to the aerodrome and you'd have to get in the queue, along with everyone else, and wait till it was your turn to go over the weighbridge and unload. Anyhow, like I said, this was a year when there was a hell of a lot of wheat around the area and, when me and my brother took a load out there this particular day, there was such a line-up of trucks, waiting to be unloaded, we decided that here was the chance to do some much-needed work on the truck. So we did, and the wait to be unloaded proved to be so long that, in the end, we'd ground eleven valves, replaced one and we had a new valve seat fitted in the head, plus we ground all the other valve seats. And we never lost our place in the line-up. And that's true. That's how long it was.

Nowadays, of course, if you asked a few of the other fellers who were also out there on that day, waiting with us, they'd be more than likely to tell you that we also did a re-ring and bearing job on the truck. Though, just a word of warning: don't take any notice of them, because the vast majority of them would be fellers who tend towards exaggerating things. But that's just how stories grow over time, ay?

Another story I was going to tell you was the one about the interstate truck driver who was having it off with the wife of the proprietor of the Swinging Tit Hotel. Now, I'm not sure if you could put this in your book or not, but rumour has it that the Terminus Hotel got the name of the Swinging Tit from the World War Two days. Back then there were about four thousand Yanks stationed out at the Tocumwal Air Base, maintaining Liberator bombers. So to get the Yanks to drink in his pub, the publican employed an extremely buxom blonde barmaid and he got her to wear a very brief tank-top sort of thing and no bra. The thing was, when a Yank ordered a drink she'd have to turn around and pour the drink, then turn back around to hand it over to him. As it happened she soon worked out that the more sharp turns she made, the more tips she'd get. And so both her and the publican profited greatly from it. So that's how the name — the Swinging Tit Hotel — came about.

Anyhow, well after the days of the buxom blonde barmaid, I'd occasionally drop in for a drink at the Swinging Tit. Far too occasionally, as my dear wife was always keen to remind me. Anyway, each time this interstate truckie would come by, he'd park his semitrailer out on the blind side of the Swinging Tit, almost up on the pavement. He'd then clamber out and get on top of his load, where he'd swing himself up over the balustrade and onto the second-storey balcony. Then he'd sneak into one of the accommodation rooms there, through a window that'd been purposely left open by the publican's wife.

Meanwhile, back at the bar, upon hearing the arrival of the truckie's truck, the publican's wife would feign a headache and excuse herself by saying to her hubby, 'I've got a blinder of a headache. I'll go 'n have a lay down. Would you mind taking over the bar?'

'Yes, okay, dear,' the publican would say, none the wiser as to what was going on.

And so she'd go upstairs and get in bed with the truckie, and they'd have their way, while the unsuspecting publican was busy behind the bar.

These shenanigans went on for quite some time till a couple of the publican's mates wised up as to what was going on. So they drew the publican aside and they hatched a plan.

Anyhow, this particular time, after the truckie had arrived and the publican's wife had complained about a headache and had nicked off upstairs to get in bed with the truckie, the publican and his mates got together. After they'd allowed enough time for the truckie and his wife to settle in, the publican stormed upstairs and he started banging on the door of the room that his wife and the truckie were having it off in.

'Hey,' he called out, 'I know what's goin' on in there and I'm comin' in so watch out!'

So panicked by this was the truckie that he was out of the bed in a flash. He snatched up his clothes and he flew through the open window. When he got out onto the balcony, he took three giant steps and he leapt clean over the balustrade. It wasn't till he was mid-air that he realised that his truck had somehow been moved further down the road.

Splat!

The truckie ended up spread-eagled, flat out on the road, naked as the day he was born, along with a few broken bones to boot.

So that was the end of that little lark. No more affairs went on at the Swinging Tit Hotel after that; well, none that I knew of anyway. Though, mind you, I don't think the marriage lasted too much longer neither.

And so now to the story that I may have already told you

at some time or other. I don't know if you remember it or not, but the crux of it took place around the small village of Blighty. Blighty being also located in the southern Riverina; roughly halfway between Denny and Finley. I'm not too sure of the exact history of the place but I've heard that there used to be three large sheep stations in the area, that'd been cut up for soldier settlements after World War One. So I'm presuming that Blighty grew out of that.

Anyhow, by this stage of the game — the early to mid-'70s — the township of Blighty had shrunk to just a dozen or so people and with just the one general store, a post office, a garage and a pub. Now I have heard from someone in the know that the Blighty Hotel was built around 1941 or '42, from local mud brick. I'm not sure about the post office or the garage, but as far as the corrugated iron store goes, at the time of this story, it was owned and run by Gerald and Florence McMillan — or Gerry and Flo as they were more commonly known.

Now, if you called in at the store, say, any time after two thirty of an afternoon, before you even had the chance to say 'G'day,' Gerry would've already chipped in with, 'Are you goin' to the pub?'

Of course, the answer would be, 'Is the Pope a Catholic?'

Then he'd say, 'Well, set one up for me. I'll be over soon.'

So you'd go over to the pub and, not long after, Gerry would turn up with a couple of his mates from the post office and garage. So you'd all settle in and have a few rounds of drinks, with everyone taking turns for a shout. Then after about an hour or so Gerry would say, 'Look, fellers, I've got a bit of business to attend to over at the store. I'll be back, so don't leave me out.'

'Okay, see yer.'

But no sooner had Gerry returned to the store than, lo and behold, his wife, Flo, would rush in through the front door of the pub and take over Gerry's stool. More importantly, she'd say, 'Gerry'll be back in a tick. This one's on me.' So they didn't shirk a shout. Not once, and that's the sort of people they were. Generous to a fault and they were in perfect synchronisation.

Anyhow, Gerry and Flo would carry on like this, swapping between joining in with their mates at the pub and minding the store, till they'd shut the shop, at around 5.30 p.m. And then they'd both settle in for an evening at the pub along with everyone else. So that's the way it was in Blighty. You always got the best of both worlds — good service and friendly customer relations. Always. Without fail. And no one shirked a shout. Never.

Now, just up the road a bit from Blighty is a place called Finley, and one of the real characters of the area was a Scottish-born farmer by the name of Bill Bennett. I'd say, by this stage, Bill would've been near on seventy-five. So he was getting on a bit. The story goes that he came out to Australia with his parents when he was about seven and, even to this very day, his Scottish accent remained so broad that none of us could understand a single word he said. But his parents had done quite well and, by this stage of the game, Bill was living in sort of semi-retirement, on the original family property at Mayrung. In fact, I think by then Bill's son was managing the farm while Bill just helped out occasionally, between doing the small transporting jobs that he'd pick up around the place.

Bill conducted his part-time trucking business in an old three-ton Bedford truck that'd he had for yonks. I forget what model it was just at the moment, other than to say it'd seen far better days. But seeing how Bill now had a bit of time on his hands, and because he wasn't short of a quid, he'd always manage to do you a job at a very reasonable price. So, if anyone needed a bit of stock carting to be done, Bill was the man to see about it. Rice and wheat-carting was the same. They'd call Bill. Really, he'd cart just about anything, just as long as it was small and easily handled. As I said, he was getting on a bit, so he didn't want to overdo things, either for himself or for his old and aging Bedford truck.

Actually, just between you, me and the fence post, there were many of us who believed that there were just two reasons why Bill kept on working: one was to have an excuse for a little tipple and the other was to make enough money to ensure that he could continue to afford to have his little tipple. Not much else mattered to old Bill. So yes, the old Scot liked his grog, and he'd turn up at all the local clearing and stock sales, where he'd pick up these small carting jobs which would, eventually, finish up with him in some pub or other at the end of the day, just 'to wash down the dust'. A very dusty place is the southern Riverina, and hot and dry too.

Anyhow, this particular afternoon, Bill had picked up fifteen Border Leicester rams from the Denny sheep market and he was heading back to Finley. Now, as I said, the township of Blighty was roughly halfway between Denny and Finley, and the Blighty pub was the only watering hole along the way. The only slight difficulty was that Bill needed to do a small left-hand turn, off the main road, to get into Blighty township.

Now I forgot to mention one important point: see, Bill's old Bedford had no brakes. Well, hardly none. And what's more, everyone in the district knew that its brakes were shot, so they were ever mindful to keep a safe distance from Bill when he was driving his Bedford. The problem with the brakes was just one of those things that Bill had always meant to get fixed, but he never seemed to find the time to get around to doing it. So, with regard to a visit into Blighty, Bill had it worked out that, at a cruising speed of forty kilometres per hour — which was about the best the old Bedford could manage — all he had to do was to take his foot off the throttle at around the one kilometre mark from Blighty and he'd coast the rest of the way.

By doing that, he could easily manage the turn-off into Blighty and still have enough momentum to roll right up to the front door of the pub.

Over time, this manoeuvre had virtually become second nature to both Bill and his old Bedford. So much so that, whenever the livestock sales were on in Denny, everyone at the Blighty pub would be waiting for him to arrive and have a round or two or three, along with Gerry and Flo, the aforementioned store owners, and everyone else. So that was the plan, and, with the heat on the rise, Bill was very much looking forward to catching up with them all and having his usual tipple, or three.

Now, unbeknown to Bill, Joe Connell, a local Finley carrier, just happened to be also out on the road, heading back to Finley. Now you could describe Joe as being a 'lubricant-type sort of character, who was always up for a bit of fun'. For example, it was Joe who'd once had a difference of opinion with one of the trees in the main street of Finley. So, late one Friday night, after he'd had a few, he decided to settle the argument once and for all by setting three sticks of gelignite under the offending tree. After he'd lit the fuse, he scooted home, changed into his pyjamas, and he'd arrived back just in time to join in with the onlookers, as they'd gathered around, discussing the terrible damage that'd been inflicted upon the now uprooted, upended and dismembered tree. 'Who did this?' 'Who would do such a thing?'

'It's got me,' Joe chimed in from the back of the group.

And that was Joe, right down to a tee. His motto was, 'Never take the credit or the blame for anything.'

Anyhow, on this particular day that I'm talking about, Joe was driving back to Finley in his International 180 C-line semitrailer. It was a pretty big rig, powered by a 160 Cummins diesel. Big and powerful. And empty. He had no load on. So Joe was driving along in his International 180 when old Bill's Bedford appeared just up ahead, loaded with these fifteen Border Leicester rams. When Joe noticed that the old Bedford was starting to slow down, he realised that Bill was heading to the Blighty pub.

It was then that Joe decided upon giving Bill a little surprise. He drove right up behind the old Bedford and he gently rested the bull bar of his International 180 C-line semi up against the Bedford's back tray. Then, from a cruising speed of forty kilometres an hour, Joe pushed the speed of his International up to fifty kilometres an hour. Then up to sixty kilometres an hour. By seventy kilometres an hour, the fifteen Border Leicester rams were shitting themselves and old Bill could see that his plan of a nice tipple at the Blighty pub was rapidly evaporating. So, in a last-ditch attempt to rectify proceedings, he leaned out the driver's side window and commenced waving his fist and shouting all the profanities in the world at Joe — in his broad Scottish accent. But, not being able to understand a word of what Bill was saying, all Joe did was to reply with a friendly wave and crank his rig up to eighty-five kilometres an hour. The old Bedford had never gone so fast. Neither had the Border Leicesters. And neither had old Bill.

Then, just before the turn-off to Blighty, Joe eased back on the power, and watched as Bill and his Bedford sailed off into the distance. Down the main road towards Finley the truck went, like a shunted railway carriage on the loose, with no hope of Bill being able to pull up for at least another five kilometres. Just at that moment, Joe veered off to the left and he pulled his rig up, right smack-bang in front of the Blighty hotel.

Of course, everyone's there, fully expecting old Bill to turn up.

'Hey, Joe,' they said, 'yer haven't seen Bill Bennett, have yer?'

'Well,' Joe said, 'in actual fact I just saw him out on the main road. But he drove straight past the Blighty turn-off.'

'Geez,' they all chorused.

'Yeah,' replied Joe. 'He was really pushin' it, too. I'd say he was doin' at least eighty-five k's an hour.'

'Wow,' came the reply. 'Somethin' really must'a been the matter for him not to drop in for his usual tipple, ay?'

Of course, Joe never let on the truth of it. I mean, as I said before, that was Joe right down to a tee — 'Never take the credit or the blame for anything.'

Beltana, SA

(Outback Towns and Pubs)

Now I might've already told you this one. It's about Beltana. Beltana doesn't operate as an actual town these days, it's what's called a 'heritage town' now. It's a pretty place, right on the banks of the Warrioota Creek, in the Flinders Ranges area of South Australia. It was first surveyed way back in the early 1860s. Then in the mid-1860s Thomas Elder and Samuel Stuckey set up the Beltana Pastoral Company and they imported 100 camels, along with their Afghan drivers. They were unloaded here, at the wharf in Port Augusta, then they walked the 150 mile or so up to Beltana. And those Afghanis and their camels were used for many, many years as the main source of transporting supplies, food and passengers all throughout the Simpson Desert area.

Then in the late 1860s they discovered copper near Beltana and the population shot up to around 500. But like most of the copper mines in the Flinders, the seams were very narrow and vertical and in them days they didn't have the technology to drill vertically to any great depth. Plus, they struck water so then the whole mining thing collapsed. So it wasn't till they set up an operations centre for the Overland Telegraph Line that Beltana came back to life. Actually, the first telephone contact reached Beltana in 1874. Then in the early 1880s, the narrow gauge railway line followed the Overland Telegraph Line through and, during the war in particular, Beltana became a very busy place. In fact, at one stage there was up to sixty-four trains a week — mostly troop trains — going through from Adelaide, up to Alice Springs, then on to Darwin by road. Oh, and I must also add that, around the late 1800s or early 1900s, John Flynn set up a post for the Australian Inland Mission at Beltana and the building — the Smith of Dunesk Mission — still exists today. So Beltana's got a decent amount of history behind it, which is why it's been designated as a 'heritage town'.

But through all its ups and downs, like many of these little places, Beltana still hung onto the usual establishments, like a bakery, a shop and a pub. Now the pub was called the Royal Victoria Hotel. It was quite a substantial, solid brick building and I suspect — though I can't be a hundred percent sure — it was built of the local stone from the Warrioota Creek. It was a beautiful old building, and in the early days it seemed that the proprietors would just stay for a year or two before they'd leave. Then in 1942 a feller called Lance Nicholls purchased the pub and he remained the publican till he closed it in 1958. Actually, Lance wasn't only just the publican at Beltana, he also took on a host of other jobs including that of the grave digger; you know, the undertaker. So old Lance was just about everything.

We lived at Quorn in them days. My father, Ted Gade, had transferred from BHP in Whyalla and he went to Quorn and got a job with the Commonwealth Railways and he eventually became a loco-engine driver. Now, fortunately, as part of my life as a young feller, at times I used to travel with my father on the old steam engines through to Alice Springs and back, which was absolutely illegal. And it was on one of these trips that we were coming south with a goods train. It was the Christmas Eve day of 1955 and I can't remember the exact course of things — possibly it was a washaway — but, whatever the problem was, it held the train up and Dad and his crew were told that they couldn't proceed from Beltana for at least a day-and-a-half or two days. Of course, the train crew was pretty upset about this because they all wanted to spend Christmas Eve and Christmas Day at home with their families.

Anyhow, Dad and one of the firemen, Laurie Payne, decided to go over to see if old Lance would put on a Christmas dinner for the train crew. So, with me tagging along, they went over to the Royal Victoria and Lance said, 'No, sorry. It's not worth puttin' on a dinner fer just a few people.'

So that was it. But then, just as we were about to leave, old Lance must've had second thoughts because he said, 'Look, hang on a bit. Tell yer what, if yer'd like ter do a little job for me, I'll do somethin' about puttin' on a Christmas dinner for the train crew.'

'Yeah, that's fine,' Dad said. 'What do yer want us to do?'

Lance said, 'I've got a kerosene fridge that needs movin'.'

Now, if you remember, those bloody kerosene fridges — say a Charles Hope for argument's sake — they were very, very heavy things. But, of course, with a Christmas dinner in the offing, Dad and Payney didn't even blink. 'Yeah,' they said, 'that'd be no problem, Lance, no problem at all.'

'Okay then,' says Lance, 'come over tomorra' mornin' 'n' we'll move this fridge then I'll sort yers all out with a nice Christmas dinner.'

So Dad, Payney and me, we turned up at the pub the following morning. I was only about thirteen back then so I was too small to help move this heavy fridge. I just hung around and watched. But unbeknown to both myself and Payney, old Lance happened to have had a wooden leg and a glass eye. Yes, both a wooden leg and a glass eye. Anyway, they've got this bloody fridge and they were moving it from one room to another. Then, at one point, someone moved the thing one way and the other feller moved it the other way and poor old Lance got jammed up in the doorway. 'Crunch.' And with the force of it, old Lance's glass eye shot out on the floor then, as he tried to reach down to pick it up, his wooden leg fell off.

Well I was stunned at the sight of all this and so must've been Payney because I remember him looking absolutely aghast and calling out to Dad. 'Jesus Christ, Ted,' he said, 'I've never seen a man fall to pieces so quick in all me life.'

The Double-banger

(Shearing Stories)

I'm collecting shearers' stories myself, you know. They concentrate on a very specific field of the industry, namely the shearers' toilets, or dunnies, or thunder-boxes, as they're more commonly known.

So I guess you could call me a 'toilet-ologist' for the want of a better name. And, from having worked in the industry for many years, plus from my ongoing research thus far, I can tell you that these dunnies come in all shapes and sizes, from the completely open-air spade affair to the more modern corrugated iron or even brick construction. And, what's more, the stories relating to these constructions are also rich and varied and, mind you, they're all fair dinkum because I only collect the real-life ones.

I'll give you an example. Just recently, a shearer was telling me that one of the dunnies he came across on an outback station was just an open-style toilet over a long-drop and stretched out over the long-drop was an elevated plank that had eight holes in it. So she was an eight-seater. And this feller reckoned how a picture would've told a thousand stories because after breakfast all the shearers would rush off to the toilet before they started work. So there they'd be, out in the wide-open spaces for all to see, perched along this plank, the eight of them, sitting there, with their strides down around their ankles. Now what a sight that would've been.

But the feller went even further. See, there was a female cook with the team so the owners of the property made an extra effort to give her some privacy. What they did was that down the far end of this row of eight, they'd made her her own personal hole with a loose bit of hessian hung around it to screen her off from full view. So you can imagine when there was a big rush on, there'd be a full house and there she'd be, this female cook, sitting alongside all the men with just this little bit of hessian shielding her. I tell you, she'd have been in trouble when a nor-wester blew up.

Now, while we're talking about full houses, another feller, an old shearing mate of mine, a chap by the name of Neville Penny — poor old Neville's pretty crook at the moment — well, Neville was telling me about the time he was shearing out on the stations. And out on these places you occasionally have those big rains like they've just had up north, where you get six to eight inches and the whole outback turns into one vast lake. Anyhow, when it rains they can't shear. They can't shear wet sheep, see. But in this particular case it'd rained so much that the shearers were flooded in. They were anchored there with no way out.

So, there they were, marooned on this station and trouble struck. For some reason or other, the whole team got severely constipated. They couldn't go to the toilet and, after a couple of days, it was becoming quite a concern. A couple of days after that, it'd turned into a great concern. By the week's end, it was a catastrophe waiting to happen.

Now the toilet on this particular station was just a two-seater or what we toilet-ologists commonly refer to as a 'double-banger'. Now I don't know what that'd make the one with eight holes, an 'octa-banger' maybe. I don't know. You'll have to look that one up, yourself. Anyway, this double-banger had a rough plank elevated over a long-drop, like in the previous style. But this one at least had the luxury of a piece of hessian hung between the two holes, which provided greater privacy for its patrons.

So, of course, in this constipated, stricken state these shearers were extremely desperate to go to the toilet and they were getting more desperate as the days came and went. And, with them being stranded, like they were, there was no way of getting medical supplies out there to help relieve the problem.

Any rate, Neville said that one old feller went out and was sitting on the toilet for ages. There he was with a wretched ache in his belly and he was trying real hard, so hard in fact that he was grunting and groaning and there were tears rolling down his cheeks. Then all of a sudden there came the rush of footsteps as someone entered the other side of the double-banger. Then the old feller's ears pricked as he heard a cacophony of loud belly rumblings that were closely followed by a mute gushing sound.

'You lucky bloody so-and-so,' the old feller called out. 'I wish I coulda done that.'

'Lucky be blowed,' said the other 'I haven't got me pants off yet.'

Georgetown, Qld

(Outback Towns and Pubs)

To give you a location, Georgetown is exactly a hundred mile south-east of Croydon. Croydon being up in the Gulf country of Queensland. Then the next town, heading east, would be Mount Surprise. That'd be about eighty mile. This is in miles. I don't understand that other language. But away back in the early days, Georgetown had a big gold rush. Then a copper rush happened not long after. So that's what got Georgetown going; gold and copper. Then after the copper had run out, the area went over to beef cattle. There's some quite large stations around the area. It's not bad country either, except the Milky Creeper has crept into it, these days.

Now I don't know how big the place was, or how many pubs there were in those early days, but there was only one pub in my time. It was one of them beautiful old-fashioned two-storey places, with the wrought iron around the verandah and the bat-wing doors, like they had in the American cowboy films. All western Queensland had them back then. Then there were stables down the back of the pub where people could put their horses and that. I went through there many times back in my droving days.

Okay then, so this was during the 50s. I was going through Georgetown and I saw this sign outside town advertising a drinking donkey at the pub. From memory, the sign itself was a crude sort of painting of a donkey, with someone holding a beer, and it said 'The Famous Drinking Donkey — at the Georgetown Pub' or words to that effect. Apparently a lady had found it wandering out along the Croydon–Georgetown road. He'd been gelded. He was pretty young, but he was in a very dire situation. Very distressed and very poorly. So that's what happened and, in the end, he took a liking to beer and so he became a local identity up at the pub. People knew of him even down around Cairns and all them places. You know, they'd say, 'If you ever go ter Georgetown yer must go 'n' have a beer with the donkey.'

The publican's name was George Dickson. George was a very good friend of mine. Every time I'd go through Georgetown, I'd call into the bar and it was, 'Oh, g'day, Goldie. Good to see yer,' and he'd introduce me to everyone and sort me out with a drink straight away. We were great mates.

Anyhow, so I goes into the bar and there's the donkey having a beer with a tourist. See, the way they done it was, they'd hold up the stubby and the donkey would just guzzle it down, like there was no tomorrow. Of course, all this did wonders for George's beer sales. And, not only that, George also had a stack of film stored behind the bar and, for a price, the tourists could have their photos taken drinking with the donkey; you know, with their arm around his neck and, if I remember correctly, George had also put a couple of holes through the top of an old cowboy hat for the donkey's ears to go through. So, yeah, he was a real novelty. What's more, George was making a real killing on it. Oh, and that's right, as it turned out, this donkey wasn't only an alcoholic but he was also addicted to nicotine and after he'd had a few beers he'd go around the place looking for cigarette bumpers to eat off the floor. You know, lick them up off the floor. So this donkey not only provided George with a massive boost in beer sales and from the supply of film, it also saved a lot on George's cleaning bill.

Anyway, it was about ten o'clock in the morning when I arrived and so I said to George, 'How many's he had today?'

George says, 'Oh, about twelve or fifteen.'

I mean, twelve or fifteen stubbies by ten o'clock in the morning is a fair bit of grog because, if I remember correctly, the stubbies back then were a fair bit bigger than what they are these days. So I said, 'Boy, I couldn't drink that many in two days.'

But, that's how it went. The donkey would drink all day and night with whoever wanted to buy him a beer. Then, after closing time, George would let him out the back door and he'd stagger down to his stable to sleep it off. And then, of a morning, he'd be there at the back door, bright eyed and bushy tailed, waiting for the bar to open so he could go through the whole thing again.

Anyway, after I'd spent some time with George, I moved on. But I was later told that one day while the donkey was up at the bar, drinking with the tourists, the council came along and they dug a big trench right across the backyard, between the back door of the pub and the stables, where the donkey lived. So then, after closing time that night, when the donkey wobbled off in the direction of his stable, down he went into this trench.

Now the trench itself was about three feet wide and about nine or ten feet deep. So it was pretty deep, and it was pretty narrow. And unfortunately, when the donkey fell down the trench, it somehow fell backwards, so he ended up stuck there all night, on his back, with his legs sticking up in the air. Then, when the council fellers arrived the next day, they came across this upside-down donkey, stuck in their trench.

'Well, I'll be blowed,' they said, and they went back to the council depot to organise a crane.

Anyhow, after a lot of to-ing and fro-ing and a lot of mucking about, they eventually hoisted the donkey out of the trench. And do you know what? That donkey would never, ever drink alcohol again. True. They tried dragging him up to the bar and forcing him to drink and everything. But, no, he wouldn't touch the stuff. He'd given up the grog, totally, and so George had to go and pull the sign down.

The Expletive Dogs

(Shearing Stories)

Here's a story about how I trained me sheepdogs to take orders without sort of knowing it, if you catch my drift. It's a true one too. The two dogs in question being Dick, a border collie cross, and Trixie, a kelpie. And it's got a lot to do with me mother as well.

See, being a small farmer in the Finley area, I'd only bring in just the two shearers. Finley, if you don't know, is down near the Victorian border in southern New South Wales, near Deniliquin and Tocumwal. But, anyway, at about three or four in the afternoon, when I had to get the sheep in for the next day's shearing, I'd get me brother to give us a hand or, if he wasn't around, I'd call on one of the neighbours to come over and help out.

Anyway, on this particular day I had the shearers working and it was time to bring the sheep in. Now, for some reason that I just can't quite remember now, the brother wasn't available and neither were any of the neighbours. So as a last resort I called me mother to come across to lend us a hand.

Now, me mother was a pretty old-fashioned sort of woman, very old-fashioned, to be honest. She was what you'd call 'straitlaced', I'd reckon. I mean, she wouldn't allow any drinking or smoking or swearing in the house. Now that was a bit hard for me and me brother, very hard actually, but me mother was extremely strict about it. She was so strict in fact that she even used to throw me and the brother out of the house at 7.30 each morning and wouldn't allow us back till it was near tea-time. And what's more, it didn't matter if it rained, or it snowed, or whatever. I mean, it could be 110 in the shade and we was still kicked out of the house. Anyway, that was me mother and that's the way it was.

111

So I needed a hand this day and, there she is, as always, she's got her apron on and she's come over to help out, and she arrives just as I'm about to get the sheep into the yard.

Now, up until that point in time, I didn't realise it but I swore pretty profusely at me dogs. Most farmers do. But anyhow, I'd really let off at the dogs. Like if I wanted something done, I'd say, 'Dick, you so-and-so bloody black bastard of a mongrel so-and-so dog, get the so-and-so away back there!' And off he'd go as happy as Larry. Or I'd yell out to Trixie, 'Trixie you bloody so-and-so bitch of a thing, go and bloody well so-and-so do this or that.' And off she'd go. So there was no real problem with it. The dogs didn't mind at all.

Now, Dick and Trixie were beautiful dogs actually. They'd do anything that I told them to; very obedient they were. I guess I was pretty proud of them. But of course, you'd never tell them that. I must've told me mother how good they were at one time or another but I wouldn't have told the dogs that I was proud of them. You just don't do that to dogs, do you.

Anyhow, the thing was that me mother arrived to help out this time and she was standing there as I was about to get the dogs to bring the sheep in for the next day's shearing. But with her being there and her being as straitlaced as she was, it suddenly struck me that I'd better watch what I said, especially as far as the swearing goes. The only trouble was that I balked when I came to give the dogs their orders. 'Dick,' I shouted, then I realised that with me mother being there I couldn't call him a 'bloody black bastard of a mongrel so-and-so', like I normally did. So instead, I shouted 'Dick,' then I had to hold my mouth for a while before saying, 'get away back there!'

Now the instant that Dick heard me call his name, his ears pricked up and he took off ... but for only about three steps. Because when it came to where I left out all the swearing in the middle, well, he just stopped, sat down, and looked me up and down as if to say, 'Hang on there boss. That's not the way it's said. Where's the rest of it? I don't know what to do if yer don't give me the whole order.'

So with Dick sitting there looking confused, I then tried Trixie. 'Trixie,' I shouted, and again left out the swearing bit before I told her to, get away back!

And I'll be blowed if the exact same thing didn't happened. She took a couple of paces, froze in her tracks, then looked up at me, waiting for the complete order to be yelled at her.

So there I was, standing there with these two dogs looking up at me, waiting to be given their proper orders and me standing there not knowing what to do or how to say it, and all the bloody sheep by this stage are wandering off in all bloody directions, and there's me mother standing there in her apron, looking to the heavens and wondering what the hell's going on.

'Frank,' she said, 'what's wrong with yer dogs. Yer've always told me how good they are but they're no good. They're just a pair of duds.'

Now that was it. Enough was enough. None of this was getting anyone anywhere and what's more there was no way that anyone was going to criticise me dogs, no way, not even me own bloody mother. So with that, I let forth.

'Dick, you so-and-so bloody black bastard of a mongrel so-and-so dog, get the so-and-so away back there!' I shouted and off went Dick in a flash, barking and carrying on and organising the sheep, as happy as Larry, which left Trixie eager and waiting for her proper orders. So I yelled out to her as well. 'Trixie you so-and-so bloody bitch of a thing, go the bloody well so-and-so away back.' And off she went as happy as anything.

Now that left me standing there right next to me mother, and I knew how she'd feel about all the swearing that'd just gone on, so I turned to her to apologise. But before I had a chance to she said, 'Oh, Frank, ' she said, all in a fluster, 'now I understand why them dogs of yours weren't working properly.'

Great Ocean Road, Vic

(Outback Towns and Pubs)

My father-in-law, Colin Cooper, was one of those real gems. Col was born in Colac, spent his childhood in Lavers Hill and Beech Forest. Now, I know it's not what you'd describe as the 'outback', but he lived and worked in many small towns throughout Victoria and one of those places was out along the Great Ocean Road which, these days, is a much visited part of Victoria even though the Twelve Apostles are now only eleven. But, of course, back in Col's time, the Great Ocean Road drive wasn't as popular as it is today.

Now, I've actually forgotten the name of the town he was living in at the time but it was just a small place, just off the highway, somewhere around Lorne. And the way Col told the story was that, one day, he was working at the local garage in this tiny place. Anyhow, the garage only had the one petrol bowser, which was usually enough because customers were so few and far between. So Col was sitting in his little office sort of thing, reading the newspaper, catching up on all the horrible things that were going on in the world, when a bloke drove in. Col reckoned that the chap looked the dead-spitting image of one of the gangster types he'd seen a picture of in the newspaper; you know, European, with the black suit and dark sunglasses.

'Hey, you, fill it up'a,' this bloke called out, in a none too friendly tone.

'Okay,' says Col and he walked out of his office sort of thing and he started filling the car up with petrol.

Now, this was a long time ago so I'm not sure what the biggest and latest cars were back then but, anyway, it was something like, let's say, a Fairlane. You know, the types that either gangsters or lost rich tourists drive.

'Nice car yer got,' said Col, in an attempt to be friendly.

'Yeah, maybe,' replied the owner, obviously none too interested in anything someone like Col might have to say.

Anyhow, as Col continued filling the car, this shifty sort of bloke happened to notice that attached to the garage was an old corrugated shed which was where Col did a bit of car servicing and where he kept whatever mechanical bits and pieces he'd come across over the years. 'You never know when a piece of junk might come in handy, do you?' — that was Col's philosophy. So when the bloke saw the shed he said, 'You wouldn't happen to have'a spare hubcap for'a car like'a mine, would you? I've'a lost d' one on d' front'a driver's side.'

Of course, being one of the latest model Fairlanes, there was no way that Col would've had one but, anyhow, Col said, 'Maybe. I'll have a bit of a poke around after I've finished filling up your car.'

'Yeah, okay,' said the bloke. Then he said, 'Well, look'a, while you're doing all that I might'a go 'n' have'a bit of' a look 'round this'a dump.'

Well, to call the town a dump sort of hurt Col a bit. I mean, he wasn't what you'd call one of those real sensitive types but this was the place where he and his wife had lived for yonks. They'd raised kids and everything there. It was a good, friendly community. No crime. Great lifestyle. I mean, what more could you ask for? But before Col could think of anything to say in reply, the bloke had locked his car in the middle of the service way and off he'd wandered.

Anyhow, Col finished filling up the car. He knew he didn't have any hub caps to suit the latest model Fairlane so he went back to his little office and continued reading the newspaper.

Half an hour later, the bloke hadn't returned. An hour later, still no sign. Now, where this little town was, the petrol bowser might only get used once, maybe twice a day, and that's only when things got busy. 'But you never know, do you?' — which was another of Col's philosophies. And with having the one and only petrol bowser being taken up by this flash car, Col could see that if there was a sudden rush on petrol he'd be in strife. 'It's bad for business,' as he'd say.

But what could he do about it? Nothing, so he kept on reading the paper. The only trouble was that, the more he read of the newspaper, the more horrific the news became. And the more Col read those sorts of stories, the more peeved he got about the world in general and, in particular, the more he got peeved that some shifty-looking bastard, from God knows where, could come along in his flash car and take up the one and only petrol bowser at his precious petrol station.

Anyhow, half an hour later and Col had had enough, so he went out to the Fairlane and he took the hub cap off the back passenger side of the vehicle and he stuck it on the front driver's side, to make it look like he'd found a new one. No sooner had he done that than Col noticed the bloke coming back down the street. From the unsteady way he was walking it was obvious he'd been down the pub for the last couple of hours. Anyhow, Col held his temperament and, when the bloke arrived, he pointed to the replaced front driver's side hub cap and he said, 'There yer go. All done.'

The bloke gave a nod of recognition. 'How much'a is that?' he grunted.

'Oh, just pay for the petrol 'n' we'll call the hub-cap an act of customer relations.'

Without another word, the bloke paid for the petrol then he jumped into his Fairlane and he took off back out and onto the Great Ocean Road, leaving Col to wander back into his office and continue reading his newspaper. Yet, somehow, the world seemed like a much brighter place.

Anyhow, life drifted on in its usual manner until a couple of weeks later. It was a weekend and Col was in his little office at the garage, newspaper spread out, reading about all the terrible things that were going on in the world, when in pulls this flash new Fairlane. Out steps the same bloke — European, black suit, sunglasses — and he's not looking too happy at all.

Blimey, here's trouble, Col thinks to himself.

Anyway, the bloke has a quick shifty sort of look around the place before he comes striding over to Col who's now trying to make himself invisible behind the newspaper.

'Hey'a, mate,' the bloke called out, 'you wouldn't have another one'a them hub caps'a, would you. I gone 'n' lost the one off'a d' back passenger's side now.'

Tin Kettling

(CWA Stories)

I grew up in Beechworth, a town in north-eastern Victoria. It was a quiet little place back in the 1940s and 50s. Beechworth CWA is about seventy years old now and my mother was a founding member, so I knew about CWA from when I was very young. Then after my schooling I worked for the Victorian Forest Commission and that's when a few of us girls decided to start up what was known as the Beechworth CWA 'younger set'. With most of us working, we met at night while the 'older set' met during the day. I remember us knitting jumpers, mittens, socks and balaclavas and gloves for the servicemen in World War Two, and we also made things like macramé camouflage nets.

Then after the war, whenever the fire brigade or the football team held an event we'd help with the catering and when we ran a dance they'd help us. To make the dance floor suitable to dance on, the boys would first scrape candles over the floor, then they'd attach bags to the bottom of a wooden box and one of us girls would sit in the box and the boys would pull us over the floor to polish it. That's how we got the dance floor nice and slippery. It was a time-consuming job but well worth it. In those days everybody seemed willing to help everybody else and so when the older ladies wanted help, we'd help them out. If there was a wedding or something, the older set took care of the cooking and we younger girls would wait on the tables. That's what happened in country communities in those days.

It was a wonderful life, and we used to have so much fun. Have you heard of 'tin kettling'? Well, when a married couple came home from their honeymoon, we'd make a supper and we'd collect sticks and empty kerosene tins — whatever would make noise — and we'd wait until they'd gone to bed and we'd go around and belt the tins until they let us in and we'd all have supper together. It was like a welcome home to the newlyweds.

I remember the time that one of our CWA girls married a footballer and when they got back from their honeymoon some of us girls and some of the footballer's mates decided to tin kettle them. The girl's father owned the cafe in the main street of Beechworth and the couple were staying there overnight. So we made cakes for supper and the boys organised some sticks and tins and off we went. It was a clear frosty night, about eleven o'clock. There was no late night closing in those days and so everyone had gone to bed. It was dead quiet and then we started this tin kettling out in the street. Next thing, the girl's father opened the upstairs window and shouted, 'Get the so-'n'-so out of here.'

'Open your cafe,' we called back. 'We've got food and we've come to welcome home the newlyweds.'

'No,' he said. 'Go home.'

Then the butcher from next door, he opened his second-storey window. 'Get out of here, you've woken the baby,' he said.

Next, the man from across the road yelled out, 'You've woken everybody in the street. I've called the police.' Little did he know that his son and a daughter were with us. Then when the policeman arrived he sided with us. 'If you open the cafe,' he said to the father, 'these young people will go in and have supper with the newlyweds and then they'll go home.'

'No way,' said the father. So then the policeman, he joined in with us. Bang, bang, bang, clatter, clatter, clatter until finally the girl's father gave in. He threw open the window and said, 'Okay, anything to stop the racket,' and he let us in.

So we eventually had our supper, which was enjoyed by all, and then we went home. But we must've made quite a noise because, in the morning, the lady who lived away up the hill was heard to say, 'Did you hear the awful noise last night. I wonder where it came from?'

But tin kettling was just good country fun. No damage done. So that's when I first joined CWA. Then I married in 1953 and I left Beechworth and went to live in Myrtleford and I've been living there ever since. Myrtleford was only eighteen miles from Beechworth but the thing was, in those days, married woman weren't allowed to work in a government job. So I had to give up my job with the Victorian Forest Commission and, with my husband being a dairy farmer, I also gave up CWA to help milk the cows. Then our three daughters arrived and I didn't return to CWA until 1990, and I've been a member ever since. That's with the Myrtleford Branch and I've been their Branch Secretary, Branch Treasurer and Branch International Officer. Then in 1995 I was elected President of North-Eastern Group. I also held that position in 2000, 2003, then again in 2008. I'm currently in my last year as their Group President and, to be honest, I'll miss the action even though I'll still be involved at Branch level and will carry on as the treasurer of four other organisations in town. So I'll still be quite busy. But I'll still miss it.

As for memorable moments, I'd just like to say how forever grateful I am for the many happy years I have spent with the Country Women's Association, not only for having the chance to assist so many people in need but also for the lifelong friendships I've made over the years. To that end I was also involved in the bushfire recovery work. Unfortunately, in our area, we had two fatalities in the fires and fifteen homes were burnt down plus thousands of acres of pasture and miles of fences burnt. But being Group President, on behalf of CWA, as soon as I was allowed to enter the bushfire area I went around to visit those who'd been affected and I gave them a set of CWA recipe books and a food voucher. The food vouchers were only worth about three hundred dollars but still, it helped them purchase food and other necessities. It was a simple gesture that showed that we cared about them.

Then later on I visited all the farms that had suffered the losses of fencing, pastures and other property. In conjunction with the Victorian State Government, CWA prepared a form for the farmers to fill in and, through our network, Group Presidents went around from farm to farm asking the farmers if they wanted to fill the form in. The way it worked was that they could get a certain amount of assistance to help them repair things like their fencing. By 'assistance' I mean that they had to tell us which firms they were dealing with and then we'd make the cheque out, directly, to that firm on behalf of the farmer. By doing it that way we were confident that the money was going to the right cause and it also helped assist the firms as well.

Many thousands of dollars were given away. Other than government aid, a lot of money came in from CWAs in other states. Also, people from all over Australia donated money straight to our Victorian CWA Fire Appeal. That received a great response and I think it was because people trusted us to dispense the funds and, of course, with us being a volunteer organisation, they knew that none of their money went into paying wages or got tied up in all the red tape.

But I spent many days visiting farmers. I didn't make appointments. I just began at the top of the valley and worked my way down to each farmer, each house, and, oh, it was a heartbreaking experience. Harrowing. Everything was burnt out and so it was all sooty with the ash. And the smell, dear me. The first place I went into I thought, I don't think I can do this. But then I realised that these poor folk were just so glad to have someone come and offer them some help that I was happy to carry on. I remember at one place, I went through what remained of a front gate and I headed to a house that stood in the middle of burnt-out paddocks and out of the corner of my eye I caught sight of a billy goat. 'Oh, it's you, Billy,' I said, and he came after me. Yes, he chased me. I was just lucky that he was on a long chain. Then when I got to the house, the lady asked me if I'd like to come in and have a cup of tea.

'That would be lovely,' I said and when I sat down she said, 'Oh, you're sitting on the cat's chair,' And sure enough the cat came in and it jumped up on my knee, and, oh, it was so black from the fires that it left sooty marks all over my clothes.

Then at the next house a small dog bailed me up at a burnt-out gate and it wouldn't let me in until the owner came out. 'Don't worry,' he said, 'the dog won't bite.' And when I told him that I was going to visit the farmers further on down the valley he asked if I'd made an appointment with the next man.

'No, I haven't,' I said.

'Well, just be careful,' he said, 'and don't go inside the house because he has a licence to keep snakes and he lets them crawl around everywhere.'

So when I arrived at the fellow's house and he asked me in, I was very quick to tell him I was very busy and didn't have time.

At another place, two men were cutting some burnt trees that had fallen across a pathway so I sat on the trailer of burnt wood while the owner filled in the forms and the other chap came up and said, 'I think I know you.'

For some reason I also thought I recognised him from somewhere, too. We were both really black from the soot and ash and our clothes were filthy and so we had to introduce ourselves and it turned out that he was the Anglican priest who was there helping out.

'Oh, of course,' I said, because I'd seen him at funerals and that.

Anyhow, I spent a week going up hill and down dale, visiting farmers and, oh, the landscape was just black from the bushfires. It was so eerie and the smell was terrible. It must have been dreadful having to live with it all because I've had grown men cry on my shoulder. That's how devastating it was. And because their livelihoods were gone, one feller looked at me and said, 'I'm finished. I'm done.'

I said, 'No, you'll be right.'

Then next feller said, 'I'm gonna fix this. No fire's gonna stop my farm.'

Yes, so in many cases the good old Aussie spirit showed through. But you couldn't even begin to imagine what some of those farmers went through, and what they're still going through. I'm absolutely surprised that some of these poor people still haven't, as yet, been able to find their way through all the red tape and rebuild. It's terrible. After twelve months one young couple still couldn't get permission to replace a shed on their property so that they could return there to live. They're still having to pay rent in town and, of course, they now also have to pay storage on all the furniture that's been donated to them to replace all the furniture they'd lost in the fires. It's just lucky that people have been giving them food, just to keep them going. Oh, there's been some terrible, terrible stories of the heartbreaks and the stresses and strains. There's even been marriage break-ups.

So that's mainly the CWA work I did after the bushfires. But one funny thing: one day I got a ring from an underwear firm in Melbourne. CWA had given them my name and they wanted to donate underclothing so they asked if I'd go round to all the ladies who'd been burnt out and get the sizes of their bras and knickers. Now, it's a bit uncomfortable to just pop in and ask people that sort of personal information but, anyhow, off I went and I did it and later on the lady from Melbourne rang me and I gave her all the sizes. Then not long after that, I got a call from one of the ladies who'd been burnt out. She said, 'I got a parcel today.'

'Oh, yes,' I said.

She told me that she'd received six bras, four chemises — little singlety things — and eight pair of knickers and, 'Oh,' she said, 'I'm going to give you a pair of knickers as a present.'

'Oh, yes?' I said.

'It's an orange G-string.'

'Oh,' I said, 'no thanks.' I said, 'I don't think an orange G-string would be quite my style.'

Rhythm of Life

(Nurses Stories)

I work in these remote communities mainly because of the experience and lifestyle. The thing is, you get to go to places where most other people can't go and you do meet some amazing characters. In between remote placements, I work in a midwifery group practice in Ceduna. So one week I'd be in Ceduna, delivering babies and getting my fix of healthy women and a regular job schedule; the next I'd be out amongst the chaos of a remote community. That was the rhythm of life and by doing that I'd manage about eighteen weeks' holiday a year.

I only do six-week stints. I find that by week four I'm getting toward my limit and by week six I've reached it. It takes a certain character to be able to live in those type of communities, and because you give so much, you come out feeling exhausted. I remember idealistic me, going out to my first remote placement with the belief that I was going to make a difference and change the world. But, nah, it didn't happen, and I doubt it ever will. What frustrates me is that you're only giving bandaid treatment. In a number of these communities there's an element of people not wanting to help themselves. Like, if you refer someone to a larger town for treatment it'd be, 'Right, I've got you an appointment on this day. I've booked you a seat on the plane. I've got you all organised.' Then they don't turn up. And that really bothers me because it's a huge waste of resources and funds; just the airfares are expensive.

A much more enjoyable experience was at Numbulwar, in East Arnhem Land. Numbulwar's a small coastal community of around two hundred. To get there you fly to Nhulunbuy, then it's a couple of hundred k's south, down on the Rose River. While I was at Numbulwar I befriended two policemen. One was from Darwin, the other from Katherine. They'd schedule their days off with mine so that we'd go fishing. So Numbulwar's where I caught my first-ever barramundi. There was also trevally and queenies. We got some crab pots, and so we caught mud crabs. Any excess from our fishing exploits we'd give to the Elders or the frail ones in the community.

We had four nurses, three Aboriginal health workers and two drivers. I worked primarily as a midwife and if you wanted to speak to a doctor you'd liaise with Darwin. The accommodation was the basic compound-type. All the windows were barred, and like in most places, there was some sort of weaponry, like a block of wood or an axe, beside the bed, just in case. The front and back porches of my place were supposed to be caged in and locked, but I didn't see the point. My back door wouldn't lock so I didn't bother about locking the front. My thinking was that if someone came in the back door and the front was locked, I'd be trapped.

I always try to maintain a reasonable fitness level and I enjoy running. But at Numbulwar I couldn't run through the community, because the camp dogs would attack me. I couldn't run on the beach, because crocodiles would get me. I couldn't run on the roads out of town because of the wild pigs, and you had to be careful in the bush, because of the buffalo. So I'd sort of run around the protected inside perimeter of the airport fence. Then there were the other obstacles. Like, you'd be driving to work and you'd have to negotiate your way around a pack of dogs that were out on the middle of the road, scrapping over the leftovers of a buffalo or a pig that someone had caught. And because the people there loved their dugong, you might come across a big flap of dugong blubber. I'd seen them go out in their boats, armed with their spears. I remember asking a woman how they actually tracked down the dugong and she said, 'When they make dust in the water, we know where they are.' And I thought that was the perfect description, because when a dugong swims it stirs up the sand.

Numbulwar was alcohol-free, and the locals kept pretty much to it. And they looked after themselves. Before coming to the clinic they'd wash their hair, and their clothes were always clean and colourful and vibrant. They'd have two skirts: one they'd wear around their waist and the other would be sitting up on their shoulders, a bit like a kaftan. While I was there they were going through a ceremony. It must've been more of a happy festivity with just certain elements of men's business and women's business. I was driving around town one night and there was this guy, dressed in his red loincloth. His body was painted white and he had feathers stuck all over him, and he was walking along holding hands with his little child, and I thought, That's just so awesome.

So Numbulwar had a good community mindset. The people were a lot gentler than in a number of other places I've worked. Someone once told me it's because it's a community by the sea. And the people I worked with were great. Like in a lot of other communities, the itinerants like the schoolteachers, the police and nurses get together.

So yes, I've now worked in quite a few remote communities. Another interesting place was Moomba. Moomba's a gas-field area in the far north-east of South Australia. I met a male nurse there that I affectionately named Ginja Ninja. It's not very often that you could pull the wool over his eyes. Anyway I had a guy come in one day who said he had something in his eye.

'Okay,' I said, 'cover your good eye and look at the eye chart.'

He said, 'Well, this is my good eye.'

I said, 'What do you mean?'

He said, 'The other one's fake. It's glass.'

Anyway, I was checking out his crook eye when in comes Ginja Ninja. So I said to the guy, 'Just go along with me here.' I said, 'Hey Ginja, can you check out this guy's eye for me please?'

Ginja's like, 'Yeah, okay, no worries,' and he comes over and he shines the torch in this bloke's eyes. The thing is, if the pupil doesn't respond to light, it could well mean there's some sort of brain injury. So there's the Ginja Ninja shining the torch in this guy's eye and of course, being glass, it's not dilating. So Ginja's getting quite worried. 'How long are you going to be out here for?' he asked.

The guy said, 'Another two weeks.'

'Oh gee,' Ginja says. 'Look, I'm not so worried about the eye you've got something in, I'm more worried about your other eye. The pupil's not dilating and that could well be something serious. We might have to fly you out to Adelaide and get a specialist to take a closer look at it.'

And this guy goes, 'Well, why don't you take a closer look yourself?' and he pops out his glass eye and he hands it over.

Well, you should've seen the look on the Ginja Ninja's face. He's never forgiven me for that.

Harry

(Bush Funeral Stories)

Okay, so is this recording thing on? Good. Just a quick story. A twice-removed third cousin of mine told me this one. There was this bloke named Harry. Harry was as old as the hills. So old in fact that he was on his last legs. So he was real crook. The doctors couldn't do anything more for him in the hospice and so his wife had taken him home to allow him to die in some sort of comfort and peace and in familiar surroundings.

The house where Harry lived, and was soon to die in, was one of those small Cornish type cottages; mud thatched, worn wooden floorboards, scuffed by time, low ceilings and tight-fitting doors. A dank sort of smell hung through the place like an invisible fog.

Anyhow, Harry's wife's got him settled. He's lying in his bed and by this stage he's lapsing in and out of a coma. So the end is nigh. Enter this scene, two old dears, Mavis and Betty. They've come to say farewell to Harry. Mavis and Betty had known him for yonks. They'd gone to primary school together, way back in the '20s, and all of that sort of stuff. So Mavis and Betty take up their positions, sitting either side of Harry's bed. Like I said, he's lapsing in and out of a coma and so he hasn't much conversation left in him.

'How are you, Harry?' Mavis asks, and poor old Harry sort of stirs back to life. He opens his eyes, takes a raspy breath, and wheezes, 'Not too good.'

'There, there,' says Betty. 'No need to exert yourself, Harry. You just relax and take it easy,' to which Harry gives a bit of a nod, then falls back into his coma-like state. So then the old dears just sat there, either side of Harry, no doubt reminiscing about the times they'd shared. So, apart from the sound of Harry's raspy breathing, silence reigned.

Then after an interlude of no conversation, Betty pipes up. 'I'm a bit concerned, Mavis.'

'Oh yes?'

'I'm just wondering how they're going to get Harry's coffin in and out of that small door over there.'

'Gee,' replies Mavis, 'I hadn't thought about that.' Then she rummages around in her handbag and produces a worn and tatty dressmaking tape measure. She leans over and she measures Harry across the shoulders. 'Oh,' she says to Betty, 'how much do you think we should add on for the size of the box?'

'Well,' says Betty, 'some of those coffins are pretty bulky so I'd allow at least another six to eight inches either side.'

'Good. Okay.' So then Mavis gets up and she goes over to the bedroom door and measures its width. When she comes back, she sits down. 'Gee,' she says, 'you may have a good point there, Betty.'

That's when they hear Harry give a bit of a cough. When they glance down, he's looking up at them with an odd sort of grimace on his face. 'Oh,' says Mavis, 'so you haven't gone just yet, Harry?'

'No, not yet, Mavis. Not yet.'

'Oh good,' says Betty, 'then what would you like us to do for your wake — just plain old sandwiches and tea or should we go all out and put on a real good country spread?'

At that point Harry shut his eyes, gave the death rattle and his soul departed this earth.

Anyhow, they did somehow manage to get the coffin in and out of the house. From memory, my third cousin twice-removed thought they might've passed the empty box in through the bedroom window, then tucked Harry up into it, and passed him back out of the window, into the hearse and off they went.

So then comes the time for Harry's funeral. It's just a small graveside service with his wife and three or four of his old friends. Of course, Mavis and Betty are there, still trying to figure out how they got Harry's coffin through the bedroom door, and there was another of Harry's old mates, a bloke by the name of Ken. Like Betty and Mavis, Ken had known Harry for yonks.

Now, right from when they'd been kids, Ken and Harry had been competitive spirits. At school they were forever trying to beat each other, whether it be marbles or a marathon or which one of them had topped the class. Throughout their teenage years they'd vied for the affections of the young women around town. It was always who had the better hairdo, who had the better clothes, who had the better car. And upon every challenge Ken had come second. He was always the loser ... that was, until recently when he'd splurged his pension on his pride and joy — the latest and greatest mobility scooter. It was far better than what Harry had had when he was alive. Ken's mobility scooter was as schmick as schmick. The advertisement slogan described it as being 'a gopher with attitude' — the Ferrari of mobility scooters — right down to its mag wheels and the fox tail that hung from the aerial sticking up six feet from the back of its carry-all.

Anyhow, the graveside ceremony comes to its end and everyone's walking away from the grave, catching up on the local gossip. Mavis and Betty are busy quizzing Harry's wife as to how they managed to get the coffin in and out of the house. At that point Ken decides to drive his gopher-scooter over to the grave to say his last farewells. He parks it at the foot of Harry's grave, then looks left and right to make sure no one was listening. Then, with more than a whiff of pride he says, 'See here, Harry. Look what I've just got. I've finally gone one better than yer.'

He then leans over and picks up a clod of dirt. And, in the motion of throwing the clod on top of Harry's coffin, Ken's elbow inadvertently knocks his gopher into top gear. *Zoom.* The Ferrari gopher takes off in a cloud of dust. And for a split second it looks like it's got just enough power to do an Evel Knievel and leap over the entire length of the six-foot-deep hole.

But it doesn't, and Ken crash lands in on top of Harry's coffin. 'Hoy,' he starts calling out, 'get me out'a here.'

At that point, Mavis and Betty spin around. 'Good God! Harry's still alive.'

That's when they see a fox tail bobbing manically back at them from above Harry's grave. When they totter back to the graveside, there's old Ken, revving his schmick gopher backward and forward over the top of Harry's coffin.

'Hoy, get me out'a here.'

A Very Merry Christmas

(Flying Doctor Stories)

One year, just before Christmas, a small bush town hospital got in contact with us. They said they had an extremely ill patient and could we fly down and transport the person back for treatment.

'It's an emergency,' they said, so we headed down there straight away.

Unfortunately, by the time we arrived, landed and drove to the hospital, the patient had died. We were about to turn around and go back out to the airport to return to base when we were confronted by some members of the hospital staff.

'Could you take the body with you, please?' they asked.

This seemed to be a strange request, and we said so. Usually, if someone dies in one of these small towns that has a hospital, and that person's going to be buried there, in the local cemetery, they go straight into the morgue awaiting the funeral.

'Is the morgue full or something?' we asked.

'Yes, in a sort of a fashion,' came their reply.

We thought this was a little odd so we asked what they meant by their morgue being full 'in a sort of a fashion'. Either it was too full to store the body or it wasn't. Fashion had nothing to do with it. And if it was full, what kind of disaster had occurred in the town? What's more, why hadn't the Royal Flying Doctor Service been notified about it?

'What's happened then?' we asked, thinking the worst. 'A plague? A bus accident, perhaps? Shootings?'

'Something like that,' they said.

'Well?' we asked.

'Well, what?' they replied.

'Well, what sort of disaster's happened that's caused the morgue to be too full to put the body in it and why haven't we been informed?'

'Look, fellers, where's your good will?' they pleaded. 'It's almost Christmas and it'd help relieve the town of a potentially disastrous situation if you just took the body back with you and we could arrange to pick it up, say, in the New Year.'

This intrigued us even more so we decided to investigate. And it was only then that the extent of the potentially disastrous situation was revealed. The staff were right. There was no possible way that the body could have fitted into the hospital morgue. Not on your life. It was chock-a-block full of the town's supply of Christmas beer.

George

(School Stories)

I was raised on a dairy farm at a place in South Australia called Monteith. You'll find it on the Murray River, roughly halfway between Murray Bridge and Tailem Bend. Back in those days it was a very busy place, especially along the river flats and around the wharf area. These days, of course, it's not like it used to be.

Monteith Primary School was my first school. It was pretty boring, really. This was back in the era when teachers could wield the willow and I guess I got into the usual sorts of trouble young boys did, so I copped my fair share. It was basically a one-teacher school but the year I began we had sixty-three children and so the teacher chap roped his wife in to help out. She taught Grades 1, 2 and 3 and he taught the rest.

I guess, for me, the only real highlight — if you'd call it that — was that I was left-handed. Of course, in those days, if you were left-handed they tried to teach you to become right-handed. So if I got caught using my left hand I'd get a whack over the knuckles with a ruler or worse. I tell you, I used to come home black and blue at times. Now I've never actually delved deep enough into it to be exactly sure but, through different things I've heard and read, if you're left-handed then apparently you use different parts of your brain. Perhaps that's why a lot of left-handers are bank managers and so forth. I'm not a bank manager but that's just one of the theories anyway.

As for memories about my primary school days, I've got a few. I guess the main one was when the 1956 floods came through and the school ended up being surrounded by water, so they shut it down and we were taken by bus to Murray Bridge Primary School for a whole year. It was a pretty big flood. Most of the dairy farms around Monteith were flooded and the farmers had to agist their cattle out to various locations. We were very fortunate in as much as our actual milking shed was just above the flood waterline so we were still able to use that. Though because of all the water, we had to bring in heaps of fodder.

But it's not so much my primary school years that I want to talk about, it's more about going to high school at Murray Bridge. It made for quite a long day really. Each morning us kids had to ride our pushbikes three or four miles out to the railway siding just to catch the 8 o'clock train to Murray Bridge. To put it into context, in those days there were a large amount of navvies and labourers working for the railways; you know, fettlers and people like that. Anyhow the railways used to run an early morning train, out from Murray Bridge, to take their workers to Tailem Bend. Then on its return trip, that same train, it'd pick up all us kids and it'd get into Murray Bridge in time enough for us to walk the fifteen or twenty minutes to the school. The same thing happened after school. The train would leave Murray Bridge and drop us kids off, on its way out to pick up the workers at Tailem Bend. It was a steam engine back then and it only had about four carriages; a couple for us boys and a couple of carriages for the girls. That's because we weren't supposed to co-mingle. Anyhow there was always a certain amount of banter going on, on this train to and from Murray Bridge and when I read in your last book about how you were writing school days stories I thought, Well, you might just be interested in this one.

See this was back when we still had Guy Fawkes Night and you could purchase firecrackers. So before we caught the train to go home after school, most of us kids had time enough to go to the shops and buy a drink or something to eat, or to purchase something that was needed at home. In those days most of us carried what was commonly called a kit bag, whereas today the kids have backpacks. Anyhow, in your kit bag you kept all your school books and you might have a tin as a lunchbox.

But there were some real characters. This particular guy I'm going to tell you about, his nickname was George. His actual name was Trevor but everyone called him George for some unknown reason. But he was one of those kids who could be hyped up into performing just about anything you wanted him to do. You know, he was as slow as a wet week but, if it was sports day and he was running the 880 yards, with everyone egging him on he'd get so hyped up that he'd perform above himself. It was like he'd go into overdrive.

Anyhow, it was around Guy Fawkes time and George had purchased some firecrackers. Back then you could buy some amazing stuff: Chinese lanterns, cartwheels and all sorts of firecrackers. But George was particularly proud of the fact that he'd just purchased these sixpenny bungers. I'm not sure how many he'd bought but he told us that he'd saved up all year for them. So there might've been a few. Now, I don't know if you remember the sixpenny bunger but they were quite a large fire cracker. What's more, they packed a fair amount of punch. So we get on the train and, of course, George says, 'Look at what I've got,' and he opens up a brown paper bag and he takes out one of these sixpenny bungers to show us. Huge it was.

"'N' how big of a bang do yer reckon that'd make, George?' someone asked.

'Lots,' says George.

'Bet it doesn't,' says someone, egging him on.

'Bet it does,' says George.

'Go on. Show us.'

'Yeah, okay,' says George.

Now I just can't remember where the matches came from — probably from one of the kids that smoked, I guess — but anyway, in a flash, someone had handed this box of matches over to George.

'Go on,' someone says. It could've been me.

'Okay,' says George and he takes out a match and he lights the wick of this sixpenny bunger.

Now also on the train in those days were the older students. They usually stayed away from us younger kids, in the other carriage. But some of them were prefects and, as such, it was their job to take it in turns to patrol the carriages in an attempt to keep things in some sort of respectable order. So George had just lit this sixpenny bunger when one of the prefects appears out of the other carriage. In an instant George sticks the lit bunger back into the brown paper bag, along with all his unlit sixpenny bungers. He sticks the bag in his knapsack and he slips it under his seat, out of view. Of course, the prefect catches a whiff of burning wick, doesn't he? And seeing that George looks the most guilty out of the lot of us, he goes over to George.

'What's goin' on, George?'

'Nuffin',' says George.

Meanwhile there's this hissing sound coming out from under George's seat. The wick's burning away, and it's caught onto the remainder of George's precious sixpenny bungers.

'Are you sure?' says the prefect.

'Yep,' mumbles George.

No sooner had George uttered those words than there came an enormous explosion from under his seat. 'BOOM', 'BOOM', 'BOOM', off went all of George's sixpenny bungers. Now I don't know if you've ever seen anyone shit themselves but I reckon that prefect might've shit himself that day because, as he took off like a startled gazelle, back to his carriage, I could've sworn I saw a brown stain spreading out on the back of his strides.

Knickers

(Flying Doctor Stories)

I first became aware of the Royal Flying Doctor Service through a chap called Dr Clyde Fenton. That was back during the war, like, when Clyde was the Commanding Officer of No 6 Communications Unit, out at Batchelor, which was about 60 miles south of Darwin.

At that time, Clyde was working solely as a pilot, not as a doctor. What's more, he had an excellent reputation as a pilot, one which was only surpassed by his dubious reputation of being a bit of a rogue, especially where the establishment was concerned. Clyde simply refused to obey their rules. In actual fact he didn't obey much at all. He was pretty much a law unto his own. Still and all, I must say that, in my experience, I found him to be an extremely likeable and fair Commanding Officer.

But as well as being a pilot and a rogue and, no doubt, a good medical man, Clyde was also a well-versed story-teller.

There's one story that sticks out in my mind, just for starters. This incident happened when he was a Flying Doctor, back before the war. It involved either a Tiger Moth or a Fox Moth, I can't remember exactly. But it doesn't matter because both aircraft were two-seaters. Now what I mean by the planes being two-seaters is that, in both the Tiger Moth and the Fox Moth, the pilot sat in the back seat and the passenger sat directly in front of him, in the front seat. And to make matters more difficult there was no direct means of communication between one and the other.

Anyway, one day, Clyde got a message to go out to pick up Mrs so-and-so from some station property. Miles away, it was.

This Mrs so-and-so was due to have a baby and they were keen to get her into the maternity ward so that they could keep an eye on things. So Clyde jumped into his plane and off he flew. But when he arrived, he checked this woman over and came to the conclusion that there was no real rush over the matter. In his medical opinion, she had another week or perhaps even two weeks up her sleeve.

But to save himself another long trip out to the property and back, Clyde decided to take the woman back into the hospital anyway. So he positioned her in the front seat. He made sure that she was comfortable, then double-checked that she was okay. 'Are you sure that you're okay?' he asked. 'Yes,' she replied. Then he took off to return to the base. They'd been in the air for about half an hour when Clyde noticed that the woman seemed to be in some sort of discomfort.

'She can't be,' he muttered to himself.

But the further on they flew, the more this woman's discomfort seemed to increase, and before long, there she was, twisting this way and that. Now the more that this woman wriggled about, the more Clyde began thinking that his previous diagnosis might've been a week or two off the mark. It'd happened to doctors before. You couldn't always be right. Nothing's 100 per cent certain. Perhaps the stress and vibration of the flight was bringing the baby on prematurely. But it was only when the situation reached desperation point and the woman attempted to lift herself out of the seat that Clyde's concern turned to panic.

'Hell,' he said, 'the baby's coming.'

So Clyde was left with no other option than to put the plane down, and put it down mighty quick, or there could be big trouble. Now it isn't the easiest thing in the world to put a plane down in the middle of nowhere, especially when that 'middle of nowhere' happens to be nothing but desert and scrub. So he searched around the area and the first piece of half reasonable land he came across, he took the bit between the teeth and went for it.

Now, as you might well imagine, landing a plane in those sorts of geographical conditions was a precarious exercise at the best of times. But with a woman on board who was on the verge of giving birth, Clyde was fully aware that any sudden bumps or violent shaking may well get the birthing process rolling before he could attend to the situation.

But as luck and good flying skills would have it, Clyde managed to make a reasonably smooth landing. Then as soon as the plane came to a halt he shouted, 'Keep calm. Keep calm. Breathe nice and deep. First, I'll get you out of the plane and we can take things from there.'

Then he grabbed his medical bag, jumped out and raced around to tend to the woman. It was at that point that Clyde happened to notice a strange, sheepish look on the woman's face. Now this particular facial expression caused him to do a double take.

'You are about to have the baby, aren't you?' he said.

'No,' whispered the woman.

'Then why all the discomfort in the passenger's seat?' he asked.

'Me undies got all knotted up,' she replied.

Manners

(School Stories)

One time I was teaching in a 'Special School' at a town down in the south-east of South Australia. With it being a 'Special School' a lot of the students either had some sort of disability or had come from a disadvantaged background. There could've been troubles at home or the parents might've been struggling on welfare for whatever reason. Stuff like that. So some of the kids I was working with were real little roughies. And I remember one day this little boy got really annoyed with me for some reason or other. I forget just why that was, at this moment, but this little kid, he spun around at me and he snapped, 'Piss off, Miss.'

Of course, I immediately replied with, 'Excuse me. In this school we always use our best manners when we talk to teachers and adults. So what should we say, then?'

And this little kid, well, he looked up at me all sheepish and he said, 'Well then, Miss, piss off, PLEASE.'

The First Wife

(Outback Police Stories)

I remember my first wife. I try not to, but I can't help it. She was the one I named the 'mad-knitter'. I tell you, mate, Madame Defarge, the crazy French woman from Charles Dickens's *A Tale of Two Cities*, didn't have a patch on her. If you might recall, Madame Defarge was the one who frantically knitted in front of the gallows while the French revolutionaries beheaded the royalist elite, or whoever they were. That was her — the first wife — down to a tee.

At the time of this incident we were rapidly heading towards our big split-up. We'd just been to a champagne-ie sort of breakfast do, over Deniliquin way, for the first wife's bloody quilting group and I was in a hurry to get back for the annual Finley Police and Citizens Charity Bowls Day. For those that don't know, Finley's in the New South Wales Riverina region, right down near the Murray River. Anyhow, I'd never missed the charity bowls day before and I was determined not to miss it now.

So we were driving home; the first wife's sitting there, knitting away like always — knit-one-pearl-one — when this motorcycle copper rides up beside me and he motions for me to pull over.

Obligingly I did. I ask the first wife to get my licence out of the glove box, which she did, and when the police officer arrives beside the car I wind down the window and pass it over to him. He takes a close look at the licence, then he takes a look at me, and he says, 'Sir, I clocked you going a hundred and twenty kilometres an hour in a hundred-kilometre-an-hour zone.'

I said, 'Gee, officer, are you sure? I had the cruise control set at just under a hundred.'

Not looking up from her knitting, my first wife says, 'Now, don't be silly, dear, you know that this car doesn't have cruise control.'

As I look up and see the police officer writing out the speeding ticket I lean over and say to the first wife, 'Can't you keep your mouth shut for just this once?'

Knit-one-pearl-one. She looks back at me and she says, a little louder than was necessary, 'You should be very thankful, dear, that that illegal radar detector of yours went off when it did or else you'd be done for going a lot faster than ... What was it, officer?'

'A hundred and twenty,' he says.

'Yes,' she says, 'you were certainly going a lot faster than a hundred and twenty, dear.'

Some sort of a smirk starts to spread itself over the police officer's face as he makes out a second ticket, this time for the illegal radar detector I'd only recently procured from 'Shifty' McNaughton, our local buy-anything-at-any-price supplier. So I look over at the first wife — knit-one-pearl-one — and say as quietly as possible, 'For Christ's sake, woman, keep your bloody mouth shut.'

At that moment the police officer frowns down through the window and remarks, 'And I notice that you're not wearing a seatbelt either, sir. I must remind you, there's also an automatic fine for that as well.'

I say, 'Well, you see, officer, I had it on, but I took it off when you pulled me over so that I could get my licence out of my back pocket.'

My first wife gives an audible smirk — knit-one-pearl-one — and before the police officer can take another breath, she pipes up and says, 'Now, dear, you know very well that you never wear your seatbelt when you're driving. I've told you any number of times about it but no, not you, you just refuse to wear it.'

I'd had enough, so I blurt out in no uncertain terms, 'Shut the fuck up, woman!'

The police officer interjects. 'Madam,' he says, 'does your husband always talk to you this way?'

Knit-one-pearl-one. She replies, 'Only when he's pissed.'

The Homestead

(Bush Funeral Stories)

Dot — It was such a terrible business, wasn't it, Jean?

Jean — Yes, terrible.

Dot — I mean we're only a small community, so we're all very close.

Jean — Such a terrible business.

Dot — What's more, the McTavish family were one of the first settlers to come out into this area. With the name McTavish, I think they must've originally come from Scotland or somewhere. I heard that they'd arrived out here in a horse and cart, with six kids and just a few cattle, and that was really the start of it. Then over the generations the McTavish family built up the cattle station, and that's where young Arnie comes into the story. I think he was either the third or fourth generation of the McTavishes. But whatever, he was the only boy of eight children and so when his parents retired, they handed it all over to Arnie and he really kicked it on from there, he did. As the beef industry grew, so did he and then he diversified into other areas. Oh, he had his fingers in a lot of pies, didn't he, Jean?

Jean — Yes, lots of pies.

Dot — Along the way, he bought this five-acre block just out on Snake Creek Road and that's where he built the big homestead. Huge it was. He was still single back then and so we all thought, Well, here we go, he's finally going to find a nice local girl and they'll get married, settle down, and have a big family. I mean, with the McTavishes being devout Catholics, that's what

145

we expected. Anyway, he went out with a couple of the local girls but nothing really happened; well, nothing that I know of. Did you hear of anything, Jean?

Jean — Oh, back in those early days there was some talk about young Dianne Halberd. She came from a good Catholic family. But even by then, she'd been around the block a few times, so to speak.

Dot — Oh, had she. I hadn't heard that. Dear me. So anyway, when Arnie was in his mid-thirties, he went off to Brisbane for a weekend and a few weeks later he came back with a woman in tow. And what's more, this woman was wearing a blessed wedding ring. We just couldn't believe it. I mean, she was a total stranger, and not that particularly attractive either. No one knew where she came from. But, oh, right from the start we could see there was going to be trouble. For starters he'd obviously married well below himself and she wasn't very pleasant, was she, Jean?

Jean — No, not at all.

Dot — Of course, we tried to welcome her the best we could, but she refused to join any of the women's organisations around town. She made it clear that she was far too young to join the CWA — Country Women's Association — and that she reckoned that she was too old for netball. And if we ever came across her in the street, she'd stick her nose up in the air and she'd walk straight past. So in the end, we just thought, Well, blow you missy, and from then on she more or less stayed out in the massive homestead that Arnie had built. It was just called 'The Homestead' back then. And worse still, no sign of children. But because we all liked Arnie so much we didn't say anything. We didn't want to meddle, did we, Jean?

Jean — No, we never stirred the pot.

Dot — Anyway, you know how word gets around in a small town: before long we started to hear that things weren't going too well in the marriage. Next we hear is that Arnie had moved into one section of The Homestead and this woman had moved into the other section. So they were kind of living separate within The Homestead. I mean, it was big enough. Then at about that same time, Dianne Halberd's second husband died in a car accident out on Bull Creek Road. We all felt terribly for Dianne. Yes, she'd had her ups and downs when she was younger, but she was another of us who'd come from a longstanding local family. So that was sad and at the age she was by then, just imagine having to bring up two young children all by yourself and still keep the hairdressing business going. That would've been tough on anyone.

Jean — I think he hit a kangaroo.

Dot — Anyway, next we started to see Arnie with this Dianne Halberd. They both would've been in their early forties by then and, like, she'd turn up to the football with him and he'd go to the netball. So we kind of got the feeling that something was going on, you know, on the romantic side of things, if you get my meaning. And they made such a lovely couple. What's more, Dianne's kids seemed to get on well with Arnie too. In fact, some people said that they hadn't seen the kids so happy.

Jean — Yes, there was certainly something going on there, I'd say.

Dot — But this other woman — Arnie's wife — she steadfastly refused to hear of a divorce. What's more she steadfastly refused to move out of The Homestead and, oh, we heard that they were having some terrible arguments.

Jean — Terrible.

Dot — As it turned out, the sneaky little wench didn't want to lose her share of the inheritance. I mean, that's basically all she'd married Arnie for in the first place, was for the money. There was no love there at all. It was all to do with the money. Wasn't it, Jean?

Jean — Oh yes, no love at all.

Dot — As the story unfolded, Arnie's wife then organised two hitmen to come out from Brisbane and kill Arnie. Of course, with Arnie dead and her still being legally married to him, she'd end up with the lot, wouldn't she? So that's what she did: organised these two hitmen. But we didn't know anything about that; not at that time, did we, Jean? None of us did.

Jean — No, we didn't have a clue.

Dot — Anyhow, a couple of months later, Arnie was in the pub. Now Arnie's best mate was also called Arnie. So there were two Arnies: Arnie McTavish and Arnie Brown. Arnie Brown was a single feller. He didn't have any family or anything, but they'd been mates from way back since when they were little kids.

Jean — Some said that Arnie Brown batted for the other side, so to speak.

Dot — Oh, I hadn't heard that one, Jean. I didn't even know he played cricket. But anyhow, the two Arnies used to meet up every Friday afternoon and they'd have a few drinks in the same spot, in the front bar of the pub, as they had done for years. It was a traditional sort of thing that everyone knew about.

Then one Friday evening this big black car pulls up outside the pub. And out of the car gets these two burly-looking blokes, with black balaclavas over their heads and they've got a couple of those sawn-off shotgun things, and they burst into the pub and they went straight over to where the two Arnies were drinking.

'Which one of youse is Arnie?' they shouted.

Of course, with both the Arnies being so shocked about suddenly being held up by these two gangster-gunmen, before they'd even given it a thought, they'd both called out in unison, 'I'm Arnie!' which really threw the two hitmen right off their guard. It was then that the two hitmen made an on-the-spot decision as to which Arnie they were supposed to shoot. Only trouble was, instead of shooting Arnie McTavish, they shot poor Arnie Brown. Oh, they reckoned there was a terrible mess inside the front bar of the pub. Did you see it, Jean?

Jean — No. That was before I took up drinking.

Dot — Of course, because none of us had ever seen such a flashy big black car and such strange gangster-looking people, by then a good number of us had gathered outside the pub to see what all the fuss was about. And so, after the shooting, these two hitmen came rushing back outside and they pushed us all aside and then they jumped into their big black car and they took off, back down the main street toward the highway and they headed off in the direction of Brisbane. So then, when the police finally arrived on the scene, we could all tell them what the car looked like and we could give them a pretty fair idea as to the size and so forth of the hitmen. I think someone had even taken down their car's number plate.

Jean — That was me.

Dot — Yes, well, off they went and they left a real mess in the front bar with poor Arnie Brown, dead on the floor.

Jean — Such a terrible business. They say it took weeks to scrub all the blood off the floor and apparently it was spattered all over the back wall and ...

Dot — Enough of that, Jean. You'll turn Swampy off. So then it comes time for the funeral. That would've been a few weeks after the shooting, after they'd done all the postmortems and so forth. So the whole town shuts down and we all turn up for the church service. We're like that around here. Even though Arnie Brown was single, and, as Jean said, he might've had his funny ways, he was still quite well respected around the town. But oh, it was just heartbreaking to see Arnie McTavish. You know, to have witnessed seeing his best mate get shot, right in front of his very eyes. You can just imagine.

But the thing was, he turned up to the funeral with his wife in tow. And oh, she was crying and going on, wasn't she, Jean?

Jean — Yes, like a real pork chop.

Dot — As to why she came along, we just didn't know. Of course, unbeknown to us at the time, the real reason as to why she was so upset was that the two hitmen she'd employed had botched the job and they'd shot poor Arnie Brown instead of her husband. Anyhow, if it wasn't for the performance that Arnie's wife was putting on, it would've been such a lovely service. It was held just down the road in our Catholic church. I say 'our' because most of us are Catholic around here, aren't we, Jean?

Jean — Yes — that's apart from the couple of C of E families, and then there's that other mob; you know, the Indian family. I don't know what they are.

Dot — But she's crying and going on so bad that, when it comes time for Arnie to give the eulogy, we hardly heard a word of it. Anyhow, when the service was over, we gathered outside and then we all followed the hearse the short distance over to the cemetery. And now, here's the interesting bit: as it unfolded, by this stage the police had caught the two hitmen who'd murdered Arnie Brown in cold blood. What's more, rumour has it that, when the police had offered them a reduced sentence if they told them who'd organised the hit, they were pretty quick to tell them that Arnie's wife was behind it all. So then, as Arnie Brown is being lowered into the ground, three or four police cars turned up and the police sort of took up their positions around the fence line of the cemetery.

Then, just as the graveside part of the service gets to its end, the police come over and they arrest Arnie's wife which, at that time, was a pretty big surprise to most of us, and to Arnie in particular. So that's kind of the end of the story.

But after all the hullabaloo surrounding the court case was done and dusted so to speak, Dianne Halberd and her two children moved into Arnie's homestead, didn't they, Jean?

Jean — Yes, sort of.

Dot — But the thing is; the thing that I was going to tell you right at the start was that we've got a few scallywags around town and one night in the front bar of the pub, they came up with the idea of renaming Arnie's homestead 'Killarney Homestead'. And, with no disrespect to poor Arnie Brown, by gee we had a real laugh about that.

Jean — Yes, we did. But I don't think Swampy quite gets it, Dot.

Dot — Gets what?

Jean — Kill-Arnie Homestead.

I'll Walk Beside You

(Railway Stories)

I've got three railway stories for you, okay, and they're all about slow trains. The first one came from old Bill Scott, an old droving mate of mine, and it was written up in the Stockman's Hall of Fame magazine, one time. I forget when. Now, knowing Bill, I don't know if this one's true or not but it went something like this. Do you know that song 'I'll Walk Beside You'? Well, that phrase was often used, in the south-west of Queensland, concerning the Barcaldine to Aramac train.

This train was owned, I believe, by the Aramac Shire Council. It opened in 1911 and ceased operating in 1975. But during the 1950s Bill was a guard, employed by the Queensland Railways, and on one occasion he relieved the Aramac guard for a fortnight while he went on holidays. Now, twice a week the train left Aramac at five in the morning and arrived in Barcaldine, which was 42 miles away, at three in the afternoon, and that's only if everything went to schedule. So it took ten hours to go 42 miles, meaning that it only travelled at about 4 miles an hour.

Anyhow, as the story goes, one morning, the train was on its way to Barcaldine and it came across a swaggie who was packing up his gear, ready to move on. So the train driver pulled up and said, 'Do yer want a lift?'

And the swaggie replied, 'No thanks, mate, I'm in too much of a hurry.'

So that's old Bill's story. Another one goes that the driver of that same train — the Aramac to Barcaldine train — could throw a handful of daisy seeds out from the engine and by the time the guard's van came past the seeds had germinated so much that the guard could pick the daisy flowers. Of course, seeing that the train was only about two or three carriages long, that story's definitely not true. It's only a throw-off at the slowness of the train.

Then another incident that happened with the Aramac to Barcaldine train — and this is true — was that it was a good few hours late one day and the stationmaster was concerned so he sent out a navvy crew to see what had happened. Anyhow, about 25 mile out from Barcaldine they'd had a massive downpour and, being that black soil, the train line had actually sunk a foot into the ground and they discovered that train was completely bogged. So then they had to wait for three or four days until the ground dried out before they could get the train moving again. But the funny thing was — and this is definitely true — on that occasion they didn't get a spot of rain at either Barcaldine or Aramac — not one spot — it only rained in that one particular area.

Now, the last story is also true because I was there. A steam train called the Forty-Two Up used to leave Cloncurry — that's up in north-western Queensland — on a Saturday night at around 10 pm and head for Townsville, over on the coast. I don't know why it was called the Forty-Two Up. It might've been just a codename. Anyhow, it had two passenger carriages and it had a mixed goods van as well. Now this train had a reputation in as much as it'd never been known to arrive on time — not to my knowledge, anyway. In fact, it wasn't uncommon for the thing to arrive anywhere up to eight hours late. Fair dinkum, eight hours late. And the main reason was, that this Forty-Two Up would stop at every blessed fettler's camp along the way and the driver and the fireman and the guard, they'd all get out and wander over to have a yarn with the fettlers' wives and have a cup of tea with them and so forth and so on. Then, when all that was done, they'd wander back to the train and get on their way again until they reached the next fettlers' camp.

Anyway, one time, me and a mate was on this Forty-Two Up. We were around all those little one-horse-pub towns like Nelia and Nonda, between Julia Creek and Charters Towers, where there's not much to occupy your time. All you see out the train window is big mobs of mimosa. Mimosa's a short bush. You wouldn't get one much over 10 feet, but it had savage thorns on it. Anyhow, we were going that slow that I could just about count the thorns on these mimosa bushes as they meandered by the window.

By this stage, I'm just sitting there, mesmerised by this mimosa. Then, I couldn't believe my eyes but, blow me down, the train started to pick up a bit of pace. 'This's odd,' I said to me mate. But it didn't just stop there. The old Forty-Two Up continued to pick up speed until we were really rattling along.

'Beauty,' I said to me mate, 'it's gonna make up for lost time.'

Then, just as we began to really hoot along, suddenly, the train come to a screeching halt. 'Goldie,' me mate said, 'maybe they just forgot where the brakes were fer a while.'

Anyhow, I looked out the window to see what the trouble was and here's the fireman and the driver walking back along the track and one of them had a rifle in his hands.

'Geez,' I said, 'this's odd.'

So me mate come over and we stuck our heads out the window and we seen them walk over to a dead dingo and they got out a knife and they started to scalp the thing. So that explained why the train had been going so fast, eh. They were chasing this dingo, and they had their rifles up the front, in the cabin there, and they shot the thing. Of course, back in them days there was a bounty on a dingo of about a pound, and sometimes the cocky — the property owner — would give them five pounds. But, blow me down, there I was thinking they were making up for lost time.

So anyway, all us passengers, we just sat around in the train waiting until they scalped this dingo and hung its carcass on the fence. Then when we finally got under way again, I drifted back into counting the thorns on the mimosa bushes as they passed by.

Lake Cargelligo, NSW

(Outback Towns and Pubs)

Shit, sure as eggs are eggs I'll tell you something about Lake
Cargelligo that's wrong and you'll put it in print and I'll get
heaps. Now, there was a local history called *The Dusts of Time*
but I just can't find it so I'll just have to try my best without it.
So, here goes: Lake Cargelligo is a natural lake on the Lachlan
River, about a hundred kilometres south of Condobolin. For
many, many generations, the Aborigines would've used the lake
as a food and water source. It was first discovered by whites —
by John Oxley, in fact — in 1817, though it wasn't settled until
the mid-1800s. Gold was found in 1873 but the high water table
restricted exploration. See, they didn't have the technology back
then. Around town, legend has it that there's still plenty of gold
down there. Mind you, I haven't seen any sign of it and I don't
think anyone else has either. But, you never know.

When the lake's full it covers about 1500 hectares and is
about three metres deep. So it's pretty big. In the early 1900s the
State Water Board cut channels from the river into the lake to try
and ensure permanent water for the township. Previous to that
it'd existed on a cycle of drought and flood. Unfortunately, the
community's also had the same sort of swings and roundabouts;
you know, thriving when wheat, wool and cattle are going
through good times, suffering when they aren't. And over the
years there's been a lot of suffering. So I hope that's sufficient
information, though now that there's sealed roads leading out
here, our hopes are on the rise that the beauty of the lake might
attract the tourists.

Anyhow, I was born here and we had the farm here and all that sort of stuff and, well, this happened, back in a winter about twenty years ago, when it was okay for just about anyone to go out and shoot kangaroos for dog meat. It's a true story. If you like, I can give you the names and addresses of the people involved. Actually, I had a drink with one of them tonight. But, anyhow, about twenty years ago these young bucks had gone out and they'd shot a couple of 'roos and they'd brought them back into town, in the back of their ute. Then before they went home they decided to drop into the Australia Hotel. Now, I won't mention any names but, when these young bucks arrived at the pub, there, slumped over the bar, working hard on drowning a monumental hangover, was a local identity who we'll just call 'Jack', for the sake of the story.

Of course, as in all small towns, gossip travels quickly, so these young bucks knew that Jack's wife had left him a while back. One rumour had it that his excessive drinking may've had something to do with it. Another was that some of his personal habits had gotten out of hand. Either which-way Jack remained oblivious to just about everything beyond the bottom of a schooner glass. So, knowing of Jack's post-marital predicament, these young bucks decided to play a bit of a joke on him.

Now, just off the main bar was a smaller bar, with an open fire. It was known as the Ladies Lounge because that's where the women used to go and have a shandy while they waited for their husbands to finish off whatever they were doing in the main public bar. Very patient women in Lake Cargelligo, I can tell you. All gems. Salt of the earth. They'd have to be. Then, between the Ladies Lounge and the main bar, other than a doorway, was a small servery-window, where the ladies could order drinks from the barman.

This particular night the Ladies Lounge was empty. So these young bucks went back outside and they got this dead 'roo out of the back of the ute and dragged it into the Ladies Lounge. The publican's wife, a very attractive woman, was in on all this so she went upstairs and she got an old dress and hat. She tied the dress around the 'roo, then she put the hat on its head, tucked its ears up underneath, then tied a bow underneath the chin. When all was done they propped the 'roo up against the wall, over near the fireplace. They placed a shandy on the table next to it then they turned off the lights. The room was now only dimly lit from the open fire. Then, after a couple of minor adjustments, one of the young bucks stuck his head into the main bar and he called out, 'Hey, Jack, there's a sheila out here in the Ladies Lounge who reckons she know yer.'

At hearing this, old Jack's head lifts off the bar and he comes to life, a bit.

'Fair dinkum?' he slurs.

'Yeah,' says the young buck, 'she's in here waitin' ter see yer.'

Well, all of a sudden, Jack thinks his luck's changed. A bit of a twinkle comes to his eye. A couple of months of trying to drown your sorrows can be pretty tough, especially with all the sorrows Jack had. So Jack grabs his beer, eases himself off his bar stool and he staggers around to the Ladies Lounge as fast as his legs could carry him, which wasn't fast. But he's eager, very eager. When he arrives he sees this apparition — this sheila — over in the corner, romantically lit by the flickering flames of the open fire. His heart skips a beat because what he sees, he likes the look of; the type that might just be a bit of a goer if she was chatted up right, you know, by a real gentleman like himself. To make a top impression, Jack licks his fingers and tries to flatten down his balding hair. Straightens himself up a bit. Tucks his stained pullover in a bit. Attempts to rub the toes of his thongs on the back of his pants, to shine them up a bit. Then he wobbles towards the fireplace.

When he gets there, he has to lean up against the mantelpiece that goes over the top of the fireplace. One hand's gripping onto the mantelpiece, the other's gripping on to his beer and there, just past the other end of the fireplace, is the sheila that's been waiting for him. In an attempt not to sound overly eager, Jack decides to start up a friendly dialogue. 'G'day,' he slurs, 'nice night but a bit on the chilly side, ay?'

No answer, so he decides a different tack to see if she's a city type or more the rural type. He'd been to the city once. Perhaps he'd met her there. He says, 'Do yer reckon it'll rain?'

Still no reply.

'Well, yer certainly the quiet type, ain't yer, girlie' he says, as he shuffles a little nearer. He struggles to adjust his focus. He scratches at his chin, trying to sort it all out. Then finally he gives up and he says, 'Look, pardon me, love, yer face looks familiar but, fer the life'a me, I just can't place yer.'

Faux Pas

(Bush Priests Stories)

Okay, I've got three stories here for you, but what you've got to understand is that I am no scholar of religion in any way, shape or form. I'll give you an example. A while ago I was playing lawn bowls at a place called Katandra West. Katandra West's a dairy farming community in Victoria, ten miles or so north-east of Shepparton. We were playing men's pairs, which is where two of you play an opposing pair. On the day a bloke called Bert Morris was my skipper, or just 'skip' as it's known in bowls.

Before the game I introduced myself to our two opponents. One was Father Owens and the other was a feller called Monsignor James. I'd previously played against Father Owens, so I knew him to be the local Catholic priest from Shepparton. Now, fellow bowlers are always addressed by their Christian names. In the case of Father Owen we just called him 'Father'. As for Monsignor James, he had darkish skin and a distinctively Spanish look about him so I simply assumed that 'Monsignor' was his Christian name.

Anyway, after our introductions, off we go. It was a pretty tight tussle with scores changing from end to end. But with bowls, it's not as if you're playing for a sheep station or anything; you do tend to make conversation and so during the afternoon tea break I turned around to Monsignor and said, 'So, Monsignor, what do you do for a living?'

Well, old Bert Morris just about fainted. Father Owens just about split his sides laughing and Monsignor went on to explain, in a very curt manner, that he was the parish priest at a place called Dookie. So that was my big faux pas, and that's about the extent of my knowledge about religion. And I've completely forgotten who won the game.

Now to the stories. Again they all concern a faux pas of one sort or another. The first one involves a farming community in an area called Mayrung. For those who may not know, Mayrung's in the southern Riverina region of New South Wales, heading down toward the Victorian border. To be more exact it's ten miles north of the Blighty Pub and about eighteen miles north-east of the pub at Deniliquin, or 'Deni' as it's more commonly known.

This particular event happened in the late '40s, just after World War Two, and it still brings a smile to the locals. In the main, Mayrung was settled by returned soldiers from World War One and, being so, family names such as Hall, Ball, Bell, Balentine and Johnson were prevalent. In fact many of their descendants still live in the area. Come to think of it, in my younger days I remember the Ball family as being excellent musicians who played regularly at the local and surrounding dances. And as it happens, it's the Ball family who are at the focal point of this story, along with the then Church of England minister, Reverend Jacobs.

There's no church as such at Mayrung so, after giving his Sunday service in Deni, the good Reverend Jacobs would come out and conduct a service in the Mayrung Public Hall. Afterward he'd have a Sunday lunch with the family of one of his parishioners on a rotation basis. This was important because, by doing it that way, it showed there was no favouritism toward any of the locals. It also helped in as much as the women of these families would only need to cater for him, say, about four times a year.

Reverend Jacobs was a stickler for punctuality. It was something he prided himself on. 'A minute late is a minute wasted' was a common phrase he used. Very common. It was also something that most of his parishioners at Mayrung had fallen in line with — apart from the Ball family, that is, who always seemed to arrive late for everything, including church on Sunday, much to the reverend's annoyance. Many were the times the Ball family would pile into the hall mid-sermon and cause Reverend Jacobs to take a moment to glare down at them over his glasses, give a disgruntled grunt, then continue.

Anyhow, it was a clear Sunday, following three or four days of heavy rain. Reverend Jacobs had conducted his usual service in Deniliquin then, after a short chat with the congregation outside the church, he set off in his Straight-8 Buick for Mayrung. The trip usually took about forty-five minutes. Now the bitumen road ended about four miles out of Deni then it turned into a formed dirt road. After slipping and sliding around for a further five or six miles the big Buick rounded a corner sideways and ended up hopelessly bogged in a deep table drain that ran beside the road. Of course there were no mobile phones back in those days and so Reverend Jacobs found himself well and truly stuck while his small congregation — predominantly made up of the Halls, the Bells, the Balentines and the Johnsons — not knowing of his plight, waited patiently for his arrival outside the Mayrung Public Hall.

The Mayrung service normally started at 11.30 a.m., sharp. By about midday and with still no sign of Reverend Jacobs, the waiting churchgoers were just starting to discuss if they should pack up and go home when a big muddy Buick appeared. Trailing the Buick was the Ball family, all packed into their ute. When Reverend Jacobs got out of his vehicle he looked a mess. He had his pants rolled up to his knees and he was covered in mud from the tips of his shoes to the top of his head.

Anyhow, the good reverend invited his flock into the hall where he apologised for being late. Following his apology he went on to explain his unfortunate predicament in this way: 'I was travelling along fine until I came to Bell's Corner, then the car got into a skid and I finished up bogged to the axles in the table drain near the Halls' property. As much as I tried, I just could not get the vehicle out of the bog until, thankfully, the Ball family arrived in their utility. They had a good length of rope which they attached to my Buick and so it is with much gratitude, I was pulled out by the ...'

At that point Reverend Jacobs had a sudden realisation that he was rushing headlong into the faux pas of all faux pas. What's more the congregation also saw it coming because, when he looked up, there they all were, sitting on the edge of their seats, eagerly waiting to hear an absolute clanger. But in that exact instant before the word 'Balls' had left his lips, Reverend Jacobs changed tack and burst into the song 'Just a closer walk with thee'.

But faux pas or not, even to this day the story is told in the small community of Mayrung about the day Reverend Jacobs got bogged to the axles in a table drain and he was pulled out by the Balls.

So that's the first story. The second goes like this: the new appointment to the Catholic Church in Tocumwal was Father Wright. Tocumwal's also in the southern Riverina region of New South Wales. Anyhow, Father Wright proved to have a very keen interest in horses. And as it happened one of the local church elders was a gentleman by the name of Brian Gorman. Brian was not only the chairman of the local turf club, but he also had horse-breeding stables about five miles out along the road to Barooga, on the riverside. During the course of his first weeks at Tocumwal, Father Wright consciously befriended Brian with the view of being asked to have a look around Brian's breeding stable. The invitation happened and the following Sunday after mass, the priest went out for a barbecue lunch and a look around the stables.

It was early August — a significant time in the horse-breeding cycle — and, as they walked around the stables, Father Wright showed great interest in, and spent some time talking to and patting, the brood mares and newly born foals. It was during this inspection tour that some of Brian's staff were having trouble with a young stallion who was in a stable, set at a safe distance away from the breeding facilities. It was kicking up a hell of a stink — if I can use that phrase — so much so that Father Wright couldn't help but hear the commotion. In the end it got to the stage where Father Wright explained to Brian how he'd always had a calming influence on stressed horses and he may be of help. Brian dismissed the suggestion, but Father Wright insisted. He would not be put off. He headed over to the stable where the commotion was coming from. When he got there he found a young stallion kicking the shit — if I can use that phrase — out of the stable door. The father immediately noticed the problem. The young stallion was trying to rid itself of a big leather apron that had been tied around its girth.

'Why would anybody want to put an apron on a horse?' asked Father Wright.

Brian was a bit embarrassed about the whole thing, but explained that the young stallion was so frisky and eager to breed that he kept masturbating against a post in the stable and the apron was fitted in an attempt to stop the practice.

'Well I never,' remarked Father Wright. 'Now I know why the Freemasons wear those aprons.'

Story three is a contentious one, but it's true. The priest involved shall remain nameless, but a local lad, Joe Thompson, swears to it. Again it's set in the southern Riverina where the Catholic priest from Berrigan would come out to the tiny community of Savernake and conduct a Sunday afternoon service at St Brendan's Catholic Church. Savernake's about fifteen miles east of Berrigan, out on the Riverina Highway. In fact the church itself is a magnificent brick building. It's worth a look on the internet. Just type in 'St Brendan's at Savernake' and you'll find it.

Anyhow, this particular Sunday the priest had travelled about six miles on his way out to Savernake when he got a flat tyre. Of course, he was all done up in his priestly regalia. What's more he didn't know much about changing tyres. Didn't have a clue, really. So he was stuck out there and in an attempt to seek assistance he decided to meditate to the Almighty. As luck would have it — or maybe it was divine intervention — young Joe Thompson was riding his motorbike out to Savernake to see his girlfriend. That's when he came across the meditating father, standing beside his spare tyre.

'Got a flat, Father?' Joe interrupted.

'Yes, my son.'

'Well, don't worry, Father, I work for Beaurepaires in Finley. I'll have yer back on the road in a jiffy.'

'Thank you.'

So while the priest drifted back into meditation — this time in thanks of his being saved — Joe levered off the hub cap, loosened the wheel nuts, jacked up the wheel, removed the nuts, then removed the wheel, put the spare tyre on, loosely screwed on the wheel nuts, let down the jack, tightened up the nuts, kicked the hub cap on, threw the spare tyre in the boot ... all in about two minutes.

'There yer go, Father,' said Joe, 'and if yer take a drive over to Finley next week, I'll fix the puncture for yer at mates' rates.'

Of course with the job being completed in such rapid time the priest got quite a start. He was snapped out of his reverie. 'Oh, thanks,' he said, then mindlessly added, 'Are you sure the nuts on the wheel are tight?'

In a flash, Joe replied, 'Yep, they're as tight as a nun's nipples, Father.'

Hardly before Joe realised his faux pas, the priest replied, 'Well you'd better give them another nip up then.'

Peak Hour Traffic

(Flying Doctor Stories)

Bush people are different, you know.

There's two types in our area, out from Broken Hill. First, you've got the sheep people. They're pretty urban sorts because they come to town a fair bit. Then there's the other breed, that's the cattle people. They live right out in the harsh country.

The cattle people don't get to see civilisation too much, maybe once or twice a year, sometimes even less. They're the ones you see around town with the big hats on. Slow movers they are, and they talk in single syllables. 'Yeah. G'day. How, yer, goin'? All, right.' That's because, out there, there's not many people for them to mix with, except for their own types. But that's their lifestyle and they reckon it's wonderful, and you can't knock them for that. They probably think that our lifestyle's pretty weird, and you couldn't blame them for that either, especially with all the goings-on you read about in the paper and see on the box.

But it's the isolation that makes the cattle people so unique.

There was an old bloke. His name was Joe. And old Joe was one of the cattle people types. He had been most of his life. He's gone now, God rest his soul. And what you've got to understand here is that there's a lot of these old fellers, just like Joe, who live out on these stations. They don't own the stations, like. They don't even manage the stations. Yet they've lived on the properties for most of their lives, helping out here and there, doing odd jobs, mostly as jackaroos. And a lot of them never get married but they become like family so, when they retire, they just go on living on these stations in a caravan or something.

Anyway, old Joe was a real bushie, retired he was, and he developed a medical problem which we had to keep an eye on. But when we suggested that he move into Broken Hill he dug his heels in.

'There's no way I'm gonna live in a place with street lights,' he complained, and you could tell by the steely look in his eye that he meant every word of it.

So the next best thing we could come up with was for him to move into Tilpa where we flew in regularly to do clinics. Tilpa was the ideal place. There definitely weren't any traffic lights there. Dead quiet it was. It had a population of about eleven, if you can imagine that — just a pub, post office, petrol bowser, that sort of town. But Tilpa had a caravan park, in a manner of speaking. Pretty basic it was. Nothing like the ones you see in the tourist brochures. What's more, it didn't need to be too flash either because you'd be lucky to get one or two tourists coming through every month or so, and that was in peak season.

So old Joe agreed to come in off the station so we could keep an eye on him. Which he did, and he instantly laid claim to being the only permanent resident in the Tilpa caravan park.

As I said, having the problem that he did, whenever we were up there we'd go and visit him in his caravan.

'How yer doing, Joe?' we'd ask.

'Yeah, okay,' he'd say in that real slow bushie drawl of his which didn't give us a ghost of an idea as to how he was really feeling.

Then one day we flew into Tilpa and we noticed that his caravan had gone. It wasn't there any more. So we asked the nurse, 'Where's old Joe?'

'Oh, he's shifted,' she said.

She told us that he'd moved out of town, down the road a bit. So we shanghaied a four-wheel drive and we drove out of town about 10 kilometres and there's old Joe's caravan, parked well off the road, away out in the scrub. So we knocked on the door of the caravan.

'G'day, Joe. How yer doin'?' we asked.

'Oh, okay,' he drawled.

Then we asked him how his health was, and about his problem, and all that sort of stuff.

'Yeah, okay,' he said, which was a fair bit for Joe, even at the best of times.

Then I asked, 'Joe, how come you've moved out of the Tilpa caravan park? What're you doing way out here, in the middle of nowhere?'

'Ah, it was the bloody traffic,' he grumbled. 'The bloody traffic in Tilpa was drivin' me bloody balmy.'

Dobbed In

(More Flying Doctor Stories)

Two things before we start. First, about the medical chests that all the station properties, and so forth, have. The Royal Flying Doctor Service provides those free of charge and there's about eight hundred of them throughout Western Australia and they're worth about $1200 each. Oh, I think that some of the bigger mining companies might pay for theirs.

A while ago I remember there was a doctor here in Derby, and he used to say, 'You could wait for up to five hours in a big city hospital to see an emergency doctor. Whereas, if you're in the bush, thanks to the Royal Flying Doctor Service, you can talk to a doctor within a minute on the radio or on a telephone. You've got over $1000 worth of free drugs at your disposal and, within two hours, an aeroplane, which has all the equipment you're ever going to need, will be there to pick you up. And it's free of charge, not only in this state, but anywhere throughout Australia.'

The only people the RFDS actually charge for their services are workers' compo cases and overseas insurance travellers. But the thing is, after the Flying Doctor Service gets you there, to wherever you're going, you do have to find your own way home. The RFDS doesn't bring you back. And when that happens you have the PAT (Patient Assisted Travel) Scheme to help you. I think there's a PAT Scheme in every state, though most probably it goes under a different name. Now I'm not sure, but I don't think you even have to pay for that service. You just go to the PAT clerk at the hospital and they'll organise everything for you.

The second thing I'd like to mention is just how strong the CWA (Country Women's Association) is here in Western Australia. We do a lot more than make scones and cakes and stuff and sell them at small street stalls, along with the occasional raffle ticket or two. Yes, we still do those types of things but we're also an extremely strong political lobby group. So much so that, these days, the government either run or they bow when they see the CWA coming. For example, it was through our efforts that the first remedial teacher and the School of the Air teachers were provided with a car. We also lobbied strongly for the Flying Doctor Service to employ their own doctors instead of using hospital doctors. By employing their own doctors you have greater continuity of service by properly trained people who are familiar with all facets of RFDS procedure. And that only happened five years ago, up here in Derby. So that's the strength of the CWA.

Now as for stories, most of what I remember happened during the Royal Flying Doctor radio sessions. How it all worked was that, just like in other states, we also had the infamous 'Galah Sessions' where everyone could get on the radio and chat with their neighbours and all that. They went from midday to one o'clock every day. The 'Galah Sessions' were really strong up here until about 20 years ago, which was when the telephones came through the Kimberley.

Prior to the arrival of the telephones, everything was organised through the RFDS radio. Not only were there the usual emergency calls and the medical sessions with the doctor but you also organised all your P and C meetings, all your CWA meetings, your Ag Department meetings over the RFDS radio. Plus, you ordered your cattle trucks, ordered your food through the RFDS radio system and, of course, everyone within cooee who was able to listened in.

How the day panned out was: there was a morning medical session at seven o'clock with a doctor on the other end of the radio. So if you were crook you told the doctor — along with the rest of the Kimberley — what was wrong with you or your family and, hopefully, the doctor could help treat you. If the doctor couldn't help you, it was more than likely that someone might chip in with some suggestions.

Then there were eight o'clock, eleven o'clock and three o'clock sessions where the telegrams were read out over the radio. These arrived from the post office and were read out from the RFDS base. Also, if you needed to send a message, you called in to the base on your radio and that message was then phoned through to the post office where it was sent out as a telegram.

And, of course, the School of the Air also shared radio facilities with the RFDS. In fact, Port Hedland School of the Air still have their offices combined with the RFDS. And that service was just wonderful for our kids when we were out on Gibb River Station.

But the School of the Air sessions were hilarious, mainly because the teachers couldn't see what merry-hell the kids were getting up to. I remember that twice a year all us parents who were home tutors and their kids, and the governesses and teachers would get together and attend a seminar-meeting at the Broome Camp School. And at this camp us parents used to perform skits for the teachers, just to show them what the kids got up to behind the scenes, and you'd get these new teachers watching our performances and they'd go, 'Oh my God, is that what really goes on?'

One skit we did was about a session that was called 'M and M' (Music and Mayhem). 'M and M' was held early in the morning and was designed for the kids to have some exercise. So you'd have your child sitting beside you and you'd go on the air and the teacher would tell the kid what exercise they were supposed to do, then they'd say, 'Okay, Johnny, are you jumping around there?'

And Johnny would be just sitting there looking completely bored with it all, and the teacher would say, 'Okay, then, how did you go, Johnny?'

And little Johnny would put on this huge act like he's completely exhausted and he'd huff and puff into the radio, 'Really well, Miss. That exercise was a tough one.'

Another skit we did was about when they'd send out Christmas recipes which showed the kids how to make like, you know, those milk-ball things made with apricot and coconut and all that stuff. So we'd act out how the kids would be mixing up all this squishy stuff and we'd have the 'teacher' pretend to come on the air and ask, 'Now, how are you doing out there, Jenny?'

Then we'd have the person who's playing the part of poor little Jenny, well, she'd be up to her elbows in this gooey stuff and, all of a sudden, she's expected to pick up a microphone, and say, 'I'm fine. Things are going real well, Miss.'

Of course, with the School of the Air sessions, you'd also get a very clear insight as to what was going on at all the other properties. We had one lady out on a station near Halls Creek. They were just starting up back then so things were pretty rough. You could imagine, at that early stage, they just had a shed and not much else to live in. But this lady was a real character and her boys were just so full-on, if you know what I mean. And one day this little boy who was in my daughter's class, you could hear him sounding really upset, so the teacher asked, 'Are you alright, Donald?'

'Sniff ... Sniff ... Yeah ... Sniff ... I guess so.'

'Are you sure you're alright?'

'Sniff ... Sniff ...' Then he bursts out crying, 'Wahhhh ... Wahhhh ... Mum's just hit me!'

Of course, all this is going out over the airwaves. Then another time his mother had obviously gone off to do something else and he was stuck with his school work and he got upset, so the teacher asked, 'Are you alright, Donald?'

And then you hear this little whimper, 'I need my mum.'

Oh, he was a real little character, he was. But she was too, you know. Like, the teacher would say, 'Okay, Donald, you've finished your painting now. Put it down and maybe you should put a rock on it to hold it there until it dries.'

Then you'd hear the mother shouting in the background, 'Bloody hell. Nick off down the bloody creek and get a bloody rock to hold this bloody painting down.'

And the creek's like 200 yards away or something. So you could imagine everyone who's listening in is rolling around with laughter while all this stuff's going on.

Then — and this happened quite a few times — you'd hear this great big bang coming out over the radio and the teacher would come on air and ask some kid or other, 'What's going on there?'

'Oh, it's alright Miss, we just shot a snake in the corridor.'

And all those wonderful bits and pieces would be broadcast out over the Kimberley. There was another little boy. One day he's dreaming away. You know, boys can be terrible that way, and the teacher couldn't get his attention so she said, 'Are you alright, Andrew? What's going on there?'

'Oh, I'm just watchin' all the boys [Aboriginal stockmen]. They're outside there, sittin' 'round, havin' a beer and a smoko.'

'And is that more interesting than doing your school work?'

'Oh yeah, you bet!'

So you couldn't get away with anything. One of the big ones was when one of the kids told the teacher, 'Dad's not here today. He'll be back tomorra.'

'Oh, where'd he go?'

'He's just gone over to get a killer.'

A 'killer', of course, is an animal you kill for your own meat. And, I mean, it's a well-known rural joke that if you ever wanted to find out what your own beef tasted like, you just went over to your neighbour's place and had dinner there. So here's this kid broadcasting to everyone in the Kimberley that his dad wouldn't be back until tomorrow because he was on his way over to the cattle station next door to knock off one of his neighbour's cattle.

So the kids were always dobbing you in, in one way or another, and the RFDS provided the radio.

Another one, and I'll make this the last little story; it's about a woman out at one of the stations who really got dobbed in. One time, the teacher wanted to speak to her so she said to the kid, 'Can I talk to your mum, please?'

'Mum can't come. She's busy,' the kid replied.

'But I need to talk to her. Could you go and get her, please.'

'Mum can't come.'

'Look,' the teacher said, starting to get really frustrated with the kid, 'I really need to talk to your mum.'

'Mum can't come.'

'And just why can't she come?'

Then the kid gathers up enough courage to shout back at the teacher, 'She can't come because ... SHE'S SITTING ON THE TOILET!'

Keep Your Hat On

(Shearing Stories)

Then there were old Gympie Howard from Longreach, a shearers' cook, he was, and a damn good one too. He was a character, a real old character was Gympie. He used to wake us up in the morning beating on an old ship's water tank with a big spoon, a red sort of square one, it was — not the spoon, that is, it were the tank that was square. Anyway, he'd be there banging away and yelling, 'Come 'n get it!'

Then I remember once there was a team of us going down from Blackall, here in the south-west of Queensland, out to some place away out in the sticks to do some shearing. So, there we were, driving through this property, mile after mile, with Gympie sitting in the front. Now it were always the passenger in the front that got the job of jumping out and opening and shutting gate, and on this trip there was just gate after gate after gate.

Anyway, there's a bit of a larrikin on the back of the truck and when they arrive at this particular gate, Gympie gets out and he opens it for the truck to drive through. So while Gympie's got his back turned, shutting the gate, this larrikin chap jumps off real quick and he hides under the back of the truck. Then as old Gympie was strolling back past the truck, to get back in again, this larrikin chap grabs him by the leg of his pants and growls like he's pretending to be a dog. And Jack Peth was driving the truck. Jack was a wool classer; a damn good one too, Jack was. Anyhow, old Gympie doesn't even take a look down. He just gives his leg a bit of a shake, causing this larrikin chap to let go his grip. Then as Gympie gets back into the cab of the truck he says

173

to Jack, 'Well Jack,' he says, nice and slow, like Gympie always talked, 'I reckon we're nearly there.'

'What makes yer think that?' Jack asks.

'Well,' says Gympie, 'I just been bit by a dog so we mustn't be too far from the homestead.'

And so they took off, leaving this larrikin chap behind, still laying there on the ground. He couldn't move because he were laughing so much. The others in the back couldn't say much either because they was laughing too. And Old Gympie didn't even twig to the fact that it was just this chap playing around pretending to be a dog.

But that was Gympie. Like I said, he was a real character.

Then there was the time that he had a piggery just out of Longreach and when he wasn't out with the shearing team he used to sell pigs to the butchers and all that. Anyhow, one day, he'd gone off down to his piggery and someone came along and said to Gympie's next-door neighbour, 'Hey, I'm lookin' fer a chap called Gympie Howard. Do yer know where he is?' he asked.

'He's not home,' said the neighbour. 'You'll find him down at his piggery.'

'Where's that?' asked the chap.

So the neighbour gave this chap the directions down to Gympie's piggery. 'Just go down the end of the road 'n turn right, yer can't miss it.'

Then just as the chap's about to walk away he turns to the neighbour. 'Oh, by the way,' he says, 'how'll I know which one Gympie is?'

'Ah,' said the neighbour, 'you'll know Gympie, alright,' he said. 'He'll be the one with the hat on!'

Personal Delivery

(Railway Stories)

Up along the old Ghan railway line there were all these remote railway sidings where, say, five or eight fettlers would live, and it was their responsibility to maintain about 30 miles of track — that's 15 miles to the south and 15 miles to the north of their location. Now the particular bloke who told me this story worked at a little siding called Beresford, which is about 30 miles south of William Creek. As you might be able to imagine, it was an extremely isolated existence because, for starters, out there, roads were either non-existent or were in such poor condition that not too many people had cars and, of course, these fettlers certainly didn't. Their only mode of transport was a government railway's section car, a little motor-driven maintenance vehicle that ran along the track.

To compound their isolation, trains came by so rarely that their supplies — their grog, in particular — used to run out pretty quick. And without a regular supply of grog, things looked crook. But a plan was hatched that will demonstrate the depth and brilliance of your average Australian worker, in this case a small gang of outback fettlers.

Now this gang's only communication with the outside world was through Main Control down at Port Augusta and, of course, the railways hierarchy would've taken an extremely dim view if they'd found out just how much grog these fettlers were actually drinking. So, to that end, the fettlers devised a secret code which they sent to their trusted mates in Main Control who, in turn, forwarded it on to the publican at William Creek. And this secret code informed the publican of the date and time he should watch out for their unmanned section car to arrive.

These fettlers then sat down and they calculated the exact quantity of fuel the section car would use on its 30-mile journey from Beresford to William Creek, taking into account such things as wind direction and velocity, track conditions and so on and so forth. That done, they put that exact amount of fuel in the section car, then they put a little more than an equal amount into a separate fuel can, which they placed in the section car along with an envelope that contained enough money to cover the cost of the purchase. That done, they started her up and waved the unmanned rail vehicle off on its journey.

Now as to why these fettlers sent the section car up the track unmanned, was — or so my mate told me — based on the fact that a human being would take up a hell of a lot of precious grog-space on the homeward journey. Though I'd be more inclined to think they were afraid of sending one of their mates up alone, because they knew that if he was anything like them, he'd most probably spend all the money on grog for himself and forget to come back. Anyhow, whatever the true reason, the section car went unmanned. And, of course, depending on the prevailing conditions, sometimes it ran out of fuel a bit short of William Creek, other times it'd go on a little bit, but most times it'd come to a halt pretty much on the money. And when it arrived, the publican simply went over and stacked the section car up with grog, refilled the tank from the fuel can, took his money, put it in reverse and sent it back to the fettlers — personal delivery.

Brilliant. I mean, something like that could only happen in Australia, couldn't it?

Still Life

(Outback Teaching Stories)

Having recently graduated from art school in Adelaide, I guess I was more into the conceptual side of things, more so than all that still-life stuff. I call it chocolate-box art; you know, things like landscapes and fruit in bowls. That sort of crap. Anyhow, I'd only been teaching at this small coastal town in South Australia for, oh, I don't know, perhaps just a few months or so. That's all. I was the art teacher in the local high school — still pretty raw — and the community was about to have their annual art show. A very big thing it was over that way. Now this art show was run by some of the older local women. A very conservative group they were too. Extremely conservative. I called them the 'art matrons'.

Anyhow the art matron who was at the forefront of this art show, she sort of took a shine to me and one day she said, 'Look, it's no good having a talented artist like yourself living here in the community and not joining in our local events. You really must enter into our art show this year. You'll be an inspiration to everyone and a role model to your students.'

I thought, Yeah, I guess I should do that. So I said, 'Okay, I'll see what I can come up with.'

'Good,' she said. 'That's settled. We'll give you pride of place in the showgrounds hall.' This art show was held at the local showgrounds.

So I got to thinking about what could I do. I didn't want to do a painting. I didn't want to do any of that chocolate-box stuff. I knew there'd be plenty of that anyway. Then I thought, Well,

I doubt there'll be any sculpture being exhibited so I'll make a 3-D object.

As it happened, at that time some of the kids at school were going out rabbit trapping. So I started thinking about, perhaps, making some sort of image from rabbit pelts. Rabbits were the perfect medium. They were rife throughout the area and they'd give the artwork that local feel; you know, something the farmers and such would be able to identify with. So I made a deal with these kids that I'd pay them fifty cents a skin and, over a month or so leading up to this art show, I'd gathered a stack of rabbit pelts. Mind you, I still didn't know what I was actually going to do with them, but my line of thinking was that once I started working on them, the art sculpture would take on its own creative form. As I said, I worked on the more conceptual side of things.

Anyhow, after the pelts had dried I started sewing them together and the more I sewed them together, the more erect the sculpture became and, for some strange reason, the more erect the sculpture became the more it took on the shape of a giant furry phallus — a giant penis stuffed with Dacron. Yes, it sort of developed on its own. It more or less started to erect itself, if you catch my drift. By the time I'd finished, this sculpture stood about one and a half metres tall and about eighty centimetres in diameter, and it had this sort of knobbly head on it.

Then I happened to be down the street one day, just a week or so before the art show and I run into a group of the art matrons. 'How's your piece coming along?' they asked.

'It's looking very impressive,' I replied.

'Oh,' they gushed, 'we're so excited to see it.'

So then comes the day to take it to the showgrounds. It was a tight fit getting it into the car but with a bit of pushing and probing and manoeuvring it this way and that, I eventually managed to get it in. I drove there. Then I had to get it out. As I said, it was about one and a half metres tall and maybe eighty centimetres in diameter and all furry on the outside. It was a very generous figure. So I extricated it from the car and I flung it over my shoulder and I waltzed into the showgrounds hall.

'Here,' I said. 'Where would you like me to stick it?'

Well, you could've blown all these old art matrons over with a feather. They just stood there like a mob of stunned mullets. Absolutely. Their jaws had dropped. Their eyes were agog. And they just looked. Stared. Then eventually one of them managed to lift her arm and point in a vague direction and stammer, 'Over there.'

Not long after I'd got it up people started arriving at the showgrounds and coming to see the art show. There was quite a buzz in the air ... especially when they saw my piece. It was sort of funny in a way because while, on one hand, the sculpture was an instant attraction to all the little kids, it proved to be quite the opposite for the parents. You'd see the mums come in with their little kids and zoom the kids would do a bee-line straight over to the sculpture and they'd start touching it and stroking it and cuddling it, and there'd be the mums, trying to pull them away. 'Leave it alone. Leave it alone. Don't touch it.'

'Why, Mummy?' the kids would ask.

And poor Mummy would be scratching around for a reason, 'Because ... because, it's dirty. It's dirty old rabbits' fur.'

'But we've got rabbits at home, Mummy, and we're allowed to play with them. Come 'n' pat it, Mummy. It feels real nice. You'd love it.'

And the mothers would drag their kids away, kicking and screaming, 'I want'a play with it, Mummy. I want'a take it home.'

Really, it was the talk of the art show. Though, of course, I didn't win anything. One of the chocolate-box paintings took out the main prize. A landscape or something; and after the show the old matron who'd invited me to enter ended up giving me a talking to about what was acceptable art and what was not acceptable art. Mine apparently fell into the 'not acceptable art' category ... for some reason.

Of course, no one wanted to buy it. Oh, all the kids wanted their parents to buy it but the parents weren't that keen on it. I don't think there was even one bid. So at the end of the exhibition I just had to pick it up, flop it over my shoulder, stick it in the back of my car and take it home, where it took up pride of place in my lounge room.

Then the following year I was given a warning by the head art matron. 'Now, listen, we don't want a repeat of last year's fiasco, do we?'

Not being a person who goes around intentionally offending people, I said, 'Okay, I'll do something else.'

Anyhow, I knew the walls would be filled with the usual crap but there was a big space in one area which I thought would suit some sort of art installation. Then I got an idea.

A friend of mine had very long black hair. It went right down to her thighs. Just gorgeous it was, this long, black, silky hair. So within this space in the showgrounds hall, I set her up on a chair and covered her with a large white sheet so that you couldn't see her. I then cut out a hole at the top of the sheet and I had her beautiful hair coming out and spilling down over the white sheet. Black against the white. Then, as the light shone through the windows of the hall, I began drawing her shadow on the floor and, over time, these shadows morphed into big petals and she became like a large stamen in the centre of this flower. It was fantastic really, though the old art matrons were a bit uneasy about it all because they couldn't quite work out what it was supposed to represent.

But the thing was, yet again, all the kids were fascinated. So much so that they were coming up and pulling at the hair that was flowing down over the white sheet. Of course it didn't take too long before my friend started to get pretty peeved about this. So much so that, finally, when one little boy came up and pulled her hair, he was greeted with a voice echoing out from under the sheet. 'Fuck off, yer little shit!'

He nearly fainted.

Anyhow, by then she'd had a gut-full, so she took the sheet off and she went to find a quiet spot to have a ciggie and a beer. Problem was, by now word had got around and there were people coming into the hall to have a look at the installation, only to find that it'd disappeared. So after she'd been gone a while the old art matrons became quite worried that my friend had had enough and she'd pissed off. So the art matrons got in touch with the show announcer and before long you heard his voice crackling out over the Tannoy — the loud speaker — in a wonderfully nasally Australian accent, 'Would the piece of missing public art please return to the pavilion, your presence is required.'

So that was the local art show, and I never won a prize. Never. But I made my mark — as I did at the school. See, at school, at times it was pretty tough going, especially with the boys. This was a farming community and art was definitely not their scene. Sport, yes; art, no. Anyway, there'd always been a strong rivalry between the school I was teaching at and a neighbouring high school. This particular time the neighbouring high school was having some sort of celebration. I forget what it was just now, but somehow we were invited to put in a piece of art. So I said to my students, 'Right fellers, we're going to do an installation. We want to surprise these neighbouring guys.'

So we had a chat about what we could do and we came up with a concept that the boys were keen on. In fact, they just loved it. First we got five sheep heads from the local butcher. Just the heads, with the skin and wool still on.

I said, 'Right, now we have to find some people with large freezers.'

That was pretty easy because some of the local fishermen had huge freezers. So then we got five large plastic tubs and we filled each of the tubs with water and we suspended a sheep's head in each of them, making sure we curled up their top lips to make it look like they were smiling. Then finally, to hide these sheep's heads, we tossed in a load of rose petals. When all that was done we placed the plastic tubs in one of the local fisherman's freezers and we froze the lot.

On the day of the celebration we loaded the plastic tubs onto the school bus and off we headed. We arrived, unloaded the plastic tubs, then we took out the five obelisks of block-ice from the tubs. They actually looked gorgeous, embedded as they were with the rose petals. In fact, the teachers from this neighbouring school were completely blown away by the effect, so much so that they even suggested we set up the ice-obelisks on the strip of lawn right outside their staffroom. Which we did.

Being a nice sunny day, as the ice began to melt, the rose petals floated away. We had to go back home right after lunchtime, which was lucky because, not long after we'd left, as the ice continued to melt, the first of the sheep's teeth appeared ... followed by the lips. Then as the ice melted further, the tongue appeared, then the eyes, then the ears. They just couldn't believe it. By mid-afternoon these five grinning sheep heads had appeared out of the ice. So from comments earlier on in the day like, 'Oh, isn't that so beautiful. Just look at those beautiful red rose petals'; by the end of the day it was, 'Who's gonna clean this bloody mess up? It stinks.'

And that was our gift to the neighbouring school. And for some strange reason we were never invited back again. So that was my entry into the hurdy-gurdy art scene over on the west coast of South Australia, back in the '70s. And I must've made some sort of impression because, something like twenty years later, I was over there as a visiting artist, working at a school that was just up the way from where I'd been teaching back then. I'd just arrived from Adelaide and me and my partner were standing out the front of the school, introducing ourselves to the principal, when a car rocked up and this woman got out. She took one look at me and went, 'Oh, I'll never forget that giant penis you made.'

God's Flock

(Bush Priests Stories)

Back in the late '70s–early '80s I was a patrol padre up in the Northern Territory. Anyway, one time, when I was doing my rounds, I went out to visit a bloke called Jack Chambers, out at Renner Springs. Renner Springs is about a hundred and sixty kilometres north of Tennant Creek, give or take. Jack had been involved in a road accident prior to this time where he'd unfortunately broken his neck. He could still walk like, but he could only move his head about six inches, which restricted him to quite a degree. Terribly frustrating for him it was — terribly — so I decided to keep a bit of an eye on him.

Anyhow I was driving up the track to Jack's place one time when I came across a scraggly mob of sheep. Now the last thing you'd expect to see out in the middle of the Territory is a mob of sheep so, when I got to Jack's place, I said, 'Jack,' I said, 'what are those sheep doing back down the road?'

'Oh,' he said, 'I just run a few for a bit'a meat.'

'Who shears them, then?' I asked.

'Oh,' he said, 'somebody'll turn up.'

Now the chances of someone just turning up, out of the blue, and landing on his doorstep, ready, willing and able to shear these sheep seemed a bit of a long shot indeed. What's more, the look on my face must've mirrored my thoughts because Jack was quick to add, 'Yer've gotta have faith, Padre. Yer've gotta have faith.'

Anyway, all of that was soon forgotten and we got to talking about life and the past and present and all those sorts of things.

Somewhere during our chat I just happened to mention that, before becoming a padre back some fifteen years or so, I'd been a farmer in Western Australia, and had even had a go at a little shearing. So that was that. Then about a month or so later I get a call from Jack. 'I'm in a bit of strife, Padre,' he said.

Of course I'm thinking the worst, you know, with his accident and all, and just how difficult it must be for him to cope. So my concerns were immediately aroused. 'Oh, yes, Jack,' I said, thinking he was in need of some religious guidance. 'If I can help in any way, I will. Just let me know.'

'Yer can,' he replied. 'So then, Padre, when are yer comin' out to shear these bloody sheep?'

I was kind of snookered then. 'Oh, yeah, okay,' I said, 'I'll be up that way next week.'

But that wasn't the end of the story. When I got back out to Jack's place I found that his shearing operation consisted of just the one stand, fashioned from an overhead rainwater tank. The cutter was run by an old concrete mixer which, mind you, when it was going flat out only did around a thousand revs instead of the usual three to four thousand revs. What's more, he didn't have any sharpening discs and his cutters were just about worn out.

So I ended up just about having to pluck these hundred or so sheep. And with not having shorn for over fifteen years, I was completely exhausted by the time the last of them was done. So much so that I just about had to crawl back to his house. When I reached the verandah, there was old Jack, sitting up there with a satisfied grin on his face.

'There yer go, Padre,' he said, 'I told yer someone'd turn up to shear me bloody sheep. All yer gotta do is have faith.'

We Live and We Learn

(Bush Funeral Stories)

I'd been working as a GP — general practitioner — up at Port Hedland for about a year. Port Hedland's a coastal town, about three hundred and sixty miles — six hundred kilometres — south of Broome, in Western Australia. This was in the early '70s, just as the mining boom was about to start. Anyhow, my wife and I were returning to Adelaide for a holiday. That would've been in about the March or April. We'd caught the infamous red-eye plane from Perth. During the flight I was reading the newspaper and I came across an advertisement for the position of a GP at an outback defence facility. So, as you do, I gave my wife a dig in the ribs with my elbow and, when she woke up, I showed her the advertisement. I said, 'How would you like to go there?' and bleary-eyed she replied, 'Oh yeah. All right.'

So that's what we did. While we were on holiday in Adelaide, I went and saw the Commonwealth Health Department, who were the people who ran the defence facility. I was accepted for the position of GP and we went out there in the May of 1972, and that's where we stayed for the following three years.

But the saga of coroners' cases just would not go away. With the defence facility being a hundred or so miles from the nearest large town, naturally enough the coroners weren't too keen on making the long trip out, and then back. So seeing how the local JP — Justice of the Peace — was also deemed to be the acting coroner, he used to take the advice of the doctor, i.e. me, as to whether a postmortem was required or not.

We had a number of deaths while I was there. It was quite sad really. The custom at the defence facility was that, for the three weeks around Christmas, they'd have a stand-down period. That gave the chance for those who had families in distant towns and cities to be able to get home and catch up with their loved ones and so forth. Problem being, there were a number of people who worked out there who'd migrated from other countries and so forth. And seeing how they had nowhere to go, they'd stay on at the facility and they'd just hang around the mess and do nothing but drink for three weeks straight. One particular guy who hadn't been seen for two or three days, was found dead in his room and, with Christmas being the height of summer, that wasn't a very pleasant case to deal with, I can assure you. Though, in that person's case, he already had a known illness, so I was able to sign the death certificate without the need of a postmortem and it was accepted by the 'city' coroner.

Another time, quite a catastrophic car accident occurred out on the main highway. A guy's wife died and their little boy was badly injured. When I x-rayed the woman's body, it showed up that she had multiple fractures and, with the cause of the death obviously being from the accident, again, I was able to write a death certificate without a formal postmortem having to be held. During that quite stressful time I was also caring for the young boy. As for the guy, he had a severe chest injury and so I organised for a Flying Doctor plane to come out and pick him up, and I decided to accompany him down to Royal Adelaide Hospital.

Anyhow, before we left the clinic at the defence facility, a nurse came to me and reported that, when they'd gone through the man's clothing, they'd found twenty-two fifty-dollar notes and three bags of opals. I'd say that each bag would've held around a cup full of opals. So, in all, there was a hell of a lot of money involved. Anyhow, for safekeeping, I took the money and the three bags of opals to the bank and placed them into their care until the guy had recovered enough to collect his loot. Now, something that did aggrieve me was that, after having sorted out the woman's death and looking after the boy and then organising the RFDS plane and accompanying the guy down to Adelaide and getting him settled in hospital, when I sent him a bill, the bugger never bothered paying up, nor did I receive one word of thanks for what I'd done. So I really lost out on that one.

Now, talking about losing: a few years before I'd arrived at the defence facility, the road to the nearest big town was little more than a dirt track, consisting of a myriad of corrugations, along with numerous deep potholes, which were full of bulldust. The story goes that one time, in the dead of winter, when the icy winds were blowing in from the desert, the police were called out to transport a deceased male from the defence facility down to the nearest city for a postmortem. To do the transportation, the powers that be sent out two coppers: a wily old sergeant, who had years of experience behind him, and a cocky young know-it-all constable, fresh from the police academy.

The vehicles they used back in those days were those short-wheel base Land Rovers. If you've never seen one: the short-wheelbased Land Rover is configured in such a way that, running down the back, from the driver's cabin, they had a sort of running board of seats down both sides. In between the two sides of seats there was a well, or a central space, where the passengers could put their feet. Now the length of the space from the back of the driver's 'cab' to the two back doors of the vehicle would've measured just over a metre and a half. Unfortunately, in this case, the coffin, containing the deceased male, was just a few inches longer than that metre and a half. And so, after they'd loaded the coffin, containing the deceased male, they couldn't quite close the back doors of the Land Rover. To that end they had to tie the doors down securely enough so that the coffin wouldn't fall out during the rough and rugged journey back to their homebase.

'I'll sort it out, Sarge,' said the cocky young constable. 'I topped me class in knot-tying at the academy.'

'Okay, go for it,' said the wily old sergeant and he handed the young feller a length of rope.

It's been said that it was quite a sight to see the young constable in action. What he did with that length of rope amazed all onlookers; the way he manoeuvred the rope around the back door handles with a flick of the wrist that way, then a flick of the wrist the other way, then an up and over and around like magic. When the knot had been completed, he stood back in admiration of his own handiwork.

'There you go, Sarge,' he said. 'That coffin won't budge an inch.'

'Goodo,' replied the sergeant, then they jumped into the Land Rover and off they headed, back home, across this rugged dirt road. Six hours later, when they arrived at the hospital to deliver the body, the young constable was out of the Land Rover in a shot and around the back to untie his handiwork.

That's when the sergeant heard the expletive of 'Shit!' And when he got around to the back of the vehicle, the two back doors were wide open, and the rope had disappeared, as had the coffin.

'Oh Jesus, Sarge,' the young constable said, 'I must'a got me reef knots mixed up wiff me slip knots 'n me half-hitches.'

With this being in the middle of winter, there was little chance of the body decomposing overnight and so the old sergeant said, 'Well, we'll just have to go back along the track early tomorrow 'n hope we can find the body before the dingoes get to it.'

'Yeah, I guess so,' said the young constable before adding, 'Sorry, Sarge.'

'That's okay, son,' replied the sergeant, 'we live and we learn.'

Later that evening, while the young sergeant was rechecking his manual on 'the art of tying knots', the old Sarge slipped into the Land Rover and he headed back out along the track.

The following day, at the crack of dawn, the two policemen met up outside the police station. They got back into the Land Rover and they set off to find the body of the male deceased. Which they did. About fifty miles down the track, the young constable yelled out, 'There he is, Sarge! Over there.'

And there he was. Though for some strange reason the deceased male had somehow ended up in an upright sitting position, against the only tree within cooee. On further inspection, the coffin had disappeared. Presumably it'd been snaffled by the person who'd found the body and had been taken away to be used as firewood to tide them through the cold winter nights. But even stranger still was that, when they went over to the body, the deceased man was holding a small posy of flowers in his hands.

'Gee, Sarge,' said the young constable, 'what's them flowers he's holding?'

'Well, son,' said the wily old sergeant, 'they're what's called forget-me-knots.'

Telling a Tale out of School

(Outback School Stories)

I had no experience of country life whatsoever. I was born in the city. Grew up in the city. Didn't even have any relatives who lived on farms. That was until I met my husband. He came from a station property out of Meekatharra. He'd attended a boarding school in Perth from the age of seven, and so he'd spent quite a bit of time in the city. Anyhow we subsequently met up and married and I went north with him, and we eventually ended up owning a station property in the Gascoyne region of Western Australia, called Dairy Creek, which was just under half a million acres. In those earlier days, Dairy Creek was predominantly sheep, then we did our last shearing in 1999 and after that it became totally a cattle place.

By the time we'd moved onto Dairy Creek we'd had two children — a girl and a boy. Our daughter was three and our son eighteen months. There was no school out there, of course. The nearest one would've been Gascoyne Junction, which was eighty kilometres away and it was only a primary school. The closest town that had both a primary school and a high school was Carnarvon, and Carnarvon was something like two hundred and fifty kilometres away. So that definitely wasn't an option. Our only real option was School of the Air, out of Carnarvon.

With School of the Air, I taught our daughter for her first year, which I must say was sometimes a little fraught. To this day she'll tell you that she's been psychologically scarred by having been taught by her mother. However, she hasn't seemed to have suffered too many ill effects. Then from Year 8 to Year 12 she went to boarding school in Perth. She did well there, then she went on to study naturopathy and has since done Psychology with Honours. So in spite of that first year of School of the Air with Mum, she's done well.

But teaching distance education to your own child was quite stressful and so, after that first year with my daughter, we decided to have governesses. And we had some great governesses. Excellent in fact. In the early part we had a lovely soft, gentle girl which would've been in great contrast to me. She stayed for two years, then we got a sweet girl who'd just finished school. She also stayed for two years. She placed a huge emphasis on art and the creative side of things. The next governess was musical. She played a guitar and composed a song which our children sang over the School of the Air radio. She was fun and light-hearted, so both the children got to experience yet another aspect of life from her. Then our daughter went off to boarding school and, for our son's last year of primary schooling, we got a very academic girl. But because our son wasn't at all academically inclined, they didn't really connect, and that proved to be a little tricky. For the most part he was more interested in being outside, doing something with his dad. Still, she pushed him, which was good because the next year, when he went to boarding school down in Perth, he was probably more prepared for high school than he otherwise might've been.

Of course, with living out on a property, there were always distractions and sometimes the children would run amuck. We had a big creek running past our house and if it rained, the creek would run. When that happened, at any opportunity, the kids would take off down to the creek, shedding clothes and shoes as they went. Never to be seen again. They'd go completely deaf at that point and wouldn't hear us calling them back to the homestead for lessons. So we'd end up having to take off our own shoes and traipse up the creek in search of them, and there they'd be, building dams or playing some sort of game in or around the water. It was all such a great adventure for them. Then when they were older their games involved racing down the creek in tyre tubes, with their mother's heart in her mouth, wondering if she'd ever see them again. And that was more or less the pattern of everyday life while the creek was running. It was far more exciting than having to do schoolwork and, of course, you couldn't stop them from having a bit fun, could you?

In many ways distance education had its ups and downs. On the one hand it was good to have that one-on-one teaching experience with your own children, where you wouldn't leave a subject behind unless they fully understood it. As for the difficulties of distance education: there was always the ever-present anxiety of not knowing where your child was positioned in the scheme of things, and that always left you wondering if you were teaching your child in the right way. But in general, I think the children got a solid basic educational grounding. Though mind you, when both the children were finally in boarding school, I remember thinking, Thank goodness that's over.

Now as for the way they went about their lessons — or 'sets' as they were known — they were sent out in packages from Carnarvon on the mail truck. I can't quite remember the finer details now but I think they came as two-week sets of schooling and the children worked their way through those, under the supervision of either myself or the governess. Then at the end of those two weeks your child did a test on them, which you submitted for marking and any comments or advice the teachers at School of the Air wanted to make were sent out on the following week's mail truck.

That's how it was supposed to work but, in our case, we most probably received several weeks of sets in one go, if not a whole term, because there were always occasions when the road was closed and the mail couldn't get through. Then in addition to having to do your sets of lessons, each day of the school week there was a half-hour School of the Air session over the radio.

All the various station children joined in on those. Anyhow, before those half-hour lessons began, while the kids were settling in, they'd be asked if they wanted to share any news they may have and, at times, some of those were quite revealing and funny.

There's just one little classic of a story. Mind you, this may be telling a tale out of school, and it is really only hearsay. But as folklore has it: one time over the School of the Air radio this little boy was asked if he had any news he'd like to share. Now these radio sessions are broadcast throughout the entire region, so everybody for hundreds of miles around was listening in and what's more they were well aware that the boy's mother was away, off visiting relatives or whatever. Anyhow there'd been a thunderstorm out on this little boy's property the night before.

The teacher welcomed the boy on the air. 'And have you any news you'd like to share, Tommy?'

'Yes, Miss.'

'Let's hear it then.'

'Well, Miss, there was a really big thunderstorm out here last night, Miss, and I'm very scared of the thunder.'

'Oh yes, and so what did you do?'

'Well, Miss, I went to get into bed with Daddy, Miss, and guess what, Miss?'

'What, Tommy?'

'Well, Miss, our governess must've been scareder of the thunder than me 'cause she was already in bed with Daddy!'

Dr Clyde Fenton

(More Flying Doctor Stories)

Clyde Fenton was one of the first real 'Flying Doctors'. I say that because not only was he a doctor but he was also one of the very rare ones that actually flew the aeroplane. In fact, as a pilot during the war, he had an outstanding record and he was the Commanding Officer of Number 6 Communications Unit, out of Batchelor, which was about 60 kilometres south of Darwin.

Now, I don't know whether he had a plane when he first went to Katherine as a doctor or whether he bought the plane after he'd gone to Katherine. I somehow have a feeling it was after he'd gone to Katherine that he bought himself a little plane. This is all second-hand, of course, but they say that Clyde was a real daredevil in the air. When he was up in Darwin he wasn't adverse to doing a few loop-d-loops over the airfield or taking a low skim over the outdoor picture theatre at night, to put the wind up the patrons, or even dive bombing groups who were out having a picnic.

Really, it sounded like he was a bit of a frustrated adventurer and so he was prepared to take some pretty huge risks with some of the flights that he did. Now, don't get me wrong: he was both a very good doctor and an excellent pilot and he saved many lives. I guess all those sorts of people took huge risks at some stage to get out into some of those more remote areas to help people who were in need. Still, it doesn't help anybody too much if they crash the plane on the way out or on the way back, does it? But that's the way it goes and sometimes you can't do too much about it.

Still, I find it interesting that when you look at plane crashes these days, very few people walk away from them, yet back then people did seem to survive more often, didn't they? Perhaps it had something to do with the lesser speeds they travelled at, because the planes back in those early days were made from not much more than wood and canvas so they'd rip apart upon contact with the ground, which was something that Clyde managed to do on a few occasions. I grew up at Humbert River Station, in the central west of the Northern Territory, and I heard about the time when Clyde crashed a plane out on our neighbouring property of Victoria River Downs Station and the wreckage had to be packed up and put on the back of a truck and driven all the way back to Katherine.

It's also well documented that Clyde had a running battle with anything to do with 'the establishment'. In actual fact, he railed against anything to do with authority so, of course, just the mention of the Department of Civil Aviation, or DCA, had him seeing red. At one stage the DCA changed the licensing regulations and naturally Clyde steadfastly refused to go for this new licence. He considered it was just a whole lot of 'red tape, mumbo-jumbo and hog-wash'. Then when they threatened to take away his licence he flew over the house of the boss of the DCA and dropped a few flour bombs on the place. They even tried grounding him on a few occasions. But Clyde never ever took any notice. He simply continued on flying with his old licence. He'd just fly off anyway. I mean, nobody would dob him in if he was going out into the bush to help someone, would they?

So yes, Clyde was a real larrikin, alright. There's even been a couple of books written about him and his exploits. Just an example of one of those was the story about when he received the medal. That was when he was in Katherine; he was decorated with some sort of bravery award or other that came in the form of a medal. Anyway, because it had to do with 'authority' he didn't want anything to do with it. That's how anti-government and anti-establishment he was. But anyway, all these bigwigs still insisted on coming down to Katherine to present him with this special medal. So when they arrived at the Katherine Hospital, Clyde had all the staff lined up to greet them, and that included all the Aboriginal staff, who he greatly admired. And, much to the bigwigs' surprise and shock, Clyde had made mock tin replicas of the medal he was about to receive and he'd given one to every single member of the staff to wear on their uniform for the big occasion.

Of course, that didn't go over very well. But that was Clyde, and he was tremendously admired up in the Northern Territory, not only for the good he did as a doctor and pilot but also because of his larrikin ways. He was one of those that always tried to buck the system, and we tend to admire people like that in Australia, don't we?

Off

(Flying Doctor Stories)

It's not like being a normal doctor, working as we do, away out here. You haven't got the luxury of being able to sit down face to face with a patient to make a learned diagnosis. What's more, more often than not the initial contact is carried out through a third party. So you have to be a bit of a mind reader as well as having a good grounding in the bush lingo.

Imagine, for example, a new doctor, fresh to the Flying Doctor Service with hardly any experience of bush people at all. Some bloke's taken ill, way out on a remote station somewhere. Normally, those types of males feel awkward about talking to a doctor about their problems, let alone anyone else, so the wife's the initial contact.

'Hello, Doctor, me hubby's taken crook,' she might say.

'What do you mean, crook? How crook is he?' the doctor would ask.

'Darl, the doctor wants to know how crook yer are,' she says, asking her hubby.

'Tell him I'm as crook as a dog,' comes the chap's voice.

'Doctor, he reckons he's real crook.'

'Can you give me some idea as to where he's feeling crook?'

'Darl,' she asks, 'the doctor wants to know where yer feeling crook?'

'Christ, woman, I'm feeling crook all over.'

'Doctor,' she says, 'Hubby reckons he's feeling crook all over.'

'Well,' says the doctor, 'before I can prescribe treatment, we've got to isolate the problem area, okay? So let's start from the top. Is he crook in the head?'

'Darl, the doctor wants to know if yer crook in the head.'

'What sort o' bloody question's that?' echoes the gruff voice. 'Course I'm not bloody crook in the head, woman. I'm as sane as the next bloke. Sounds to me like he's the one who's crook in the head, not me.'

'No, Doctor, he's not crook in the head.'

'Well, is he crook in the abdomen?'

'In the what?' she asks.

'The abdomen. The stomach.'

'Oh, you mean the guts!' she says. 'Darl, are yer crook in the guts?'

'Too bloody right I'm crook in the guts! That's the bloody reason I'm calling the idiot.'

'Yes, Doctor, he's crook in the guts.'

'Has he got nausea?'

'Nausea? What's nausea?'

'Has he been vomiting?' says the doctor.

'What?'

'Has he been spewing?'

'No, I don't think he's been spewing. Darl, yer haven't been spewing again, have yer? No doctor, he hasn't been spewing.'

'Well, has he opened his bowels today?'

'What do yer mean by "opened his bowels"?'

'Has he had a crap?'

'Darl, have yer done number twos yet, today?'

A loud call of 'No!' is heard in the background.

'No, Doctor, he hasn't done one of those.'

'Well, has he voided?'

'What's that?'

'Has he urinated?'

'Urinated? What's that?' she asks.

'For God's sake, has he had a piss?'

'No need to get angry, Doctor,' comes the reply. 'Darl, the doctor wants to know if yer done a number one today.'

'Tell him to mind his own bloody business!'

'He's not sure, Doctor.'

And so the conversation continues until the doctor eventually eliminates the possibilities and homes in on the problem.

But sometimes, of course, it gets more serious than that, a lot more serious. Like the time we were doing a clinic out at Thargomindah and the emergency beacon was activated on the HF radio. A station feller was calling from about three-quarters of an hour's flying time away, saying that there'd been an accident.

As it turned out, a motor cyclist was on his honeymoon and he'd been riding along with his wife in the side car. They'd come to the end of the bitumen section and hit the gravel. He'd lost control, veered off over the table drain, and his leg got caught between the motor bike and a mulga tree. His wife was okay but he wasn't. As I heard it over the radio, the station feller said that the motor cyclist had his leg broken.

To piece the situation together, I began with a few questions. Firstly, how did he know the leg was broken, to which I received the sharp reply of 'Yer'd have to be blind not to see that it's broken, Doc.' So that established that. Then I asked which leg was it, right leg or left leg? Was it broken above the knee or below the knee? 'Above the knee,' I was told. Then I asked if it was bleeding.

'Yes,' the station feller said, 'it's bleeding quite badly.'

So I questioned him about the bleeding. Was it seeping from the breakage point or was the blood spurting out?

'It's spurting out,' came the reply.

'How far?' I asked.

'Oh, only about four or five yards,' he said.

Well, that told me something. I imagined the situation again. A motor cyclist, still alive, thankfully, but in deep shock. The accident. The bike. The tree. A leg which had been broken. The spurting blood. It must surely have been a severed artery. That was the first problem we had to sort out. So, I told the station feller to apply pressure to the bleeding spot and try to contain the bleeding.

So we activated the plane and off we flew. We were met at the airstrip in a ute and driven to the scene of the accident. It was only as we drove up to the motor cyclist that the whole story was revealed. The mental picture I'd drawn was complete, apart from one major discrepancy. The station feller forgot to inform me of one very important fact about the broken leg. The leg wasn't just broken, it'd been broken completely ... off. And there was the motor cyclist, sitting under the tree, and propped up beside him was his severed leg.

Halls Creek, WA

(Outback Towns and Pubs)

This might sound like a little bit of an odd one, mate, but I'm hoping you might be able to help me out. Now, if you don't mind, I'd prefer it if you didn't mention the name of the actual town where this happened. It's just that, if me mates found out, it'd upset them. I mean, the chances are pretty slim anyway, I guess, because, if the truth be known, I don't think they've ever read a book in their lives. Same here. You know, by the time you've finished work you're usually pretty knackered and so there's only enough time for a few beers and a bit of a yarn with your mates, then go home for a bite to eat before you hit the sack. No time for reading books. Still, I guess, it'd be okay to say that the town's in the Kimberley area of Western Australia. God's own country, I tell you.

Now, I don't know much about the history of the place because me and me mates, we're just workers, out on the roads, but I think they found gold here once upon a time and also drovers used to come through this way because it's at the top of the Canning Stock Route, which has probably given the town's name away. But who gives a bugger. It just shows how desperate I am. But that's all I'm saying.

Okay, now, this all happened about a year or so ago, right. It was a Friday night and we'd knocked off from work and we were in the front bar. There was Bluey, Tail-lights, Tugga and me. The nickname of Bluey is pretty obvious, because he's got red hair. Then Tail-lights because, if there's any trouble, that's all you'll ever see of him, is his tail-lights, and Tugga, well, you can work that one out for yourself. But that's all beside the point because on this particular night there was a bloke sitting over in the corner, drinking by himself. We'd never seen him before but, to give you some sort of idea, I'd say he would've been about fifty — around our age. It was pretty obvious he wasn't a bush sort of feller. He was more city. You know, like he could've come from Darwin or somewhere, where they dress up a bit more, and he had a briefcase, so he was some sort of a business feller or other.

Anyhow, we never like to see a man drinking alone so we took him over a beer and said, 'G'day'. 'Thanks,' he said and then we got talking about this, that and the other and, somewhere along the line, I saw that he had a book there with him. So I asked him about it and it turned out to be one of yours. I forget what it was called but it was a Great something-or-other. I haven't read any of them, myself, personally, but this feller seemed to be quite a fan of yours, so that's how I remembered your name: Swampy Marsh.

Now I forget the bloke's name but the thing was that, after we got talking to him, somehow it got around to his personal life and he started telling us how he'd only recently been through a rough patch with his missus. Same old thing; she was unhappy, he was unhappy, and, you know, how, after thirty years of being married he'd started to lose the urge, so to speak. Of course, we could all relate to that. I mean, Blue had been married for about thirty years. Same with Tail-lights. I'd been married just on twenty-two years, as the wife continually reminds me. Tugga, of course, is still single. Anyhow, it seemed like the feller really wanted to talk about it, so Bluey asked if they'd split up.

'Oh, God no,' he said, 'we sorted it out 'n' now we're closer than ever.'

'How's that?' we asked.

He said, 'Well, this feller sold me a special ointment.'

'Is that right?' we said.

'Yep, heaps better than Viagra,' he said, and he sort of gave us that type of look that made it clear as to exactly what he was on about. Then he added, 'So good, in fact, that me 'n' the wife ended up buying the company that made the stuff.'

'Gee, have yer got any with yer?' asked Tail-lights.

'As a matter of fact,' he said, 'I've got a little bit left here in a sample jar,' and he pulled this small red jar out of his coat pocket. I mean, it didn't look too fancy. There was a printed label glued on it that read 'Johnson's Pawpaw Magic'. Then below that it was wrote how it was good for just about everything — including you know what — and then right at the bottom there was a telephone number.

'Open it up,' he said. 'Take a look.'

So we unscrewed the lid. Just a tiny little jar it was. The ointment was slightly greasy — a bit thicker than Vaseline — but it had a slight tingle to it. And it had a flowery sort of smell that you'd reckon a woman might be attracted to. The bloke said how it was made up from 95 per cent concentrated pawpaw and the other 5 per cent was some sort of a secret magic ingredient that — how can I say — well, if you rubbed just a little bit it on yourself, it got things up and going, if you catch my drift.

'No kiddin',' we said.

'As true as I stand here,' says the bloke.

So, naturally, we were pretty keen on getting ourselves a jar.

'Gee, you'll be lucky,' the bloke said. 'I sold out in Broome, in only two days, 'n' I'm just on my way back to Darwin to pick up another batch.'

But, anyhow, he dug around in his briefcase and, as luck would have it, he found four sample jars. That's all he had left; just the four sample jars.

'So how much is it?' asked Blue.

'Oh,' he said, 'a sample jar like this retails for around a hundred dollars.'

'A hundred fuckin' dollars,' says Tugga. 'Christ, yer could buy a hell-of-a-lot'a beer fer a hundred dollars.'

Then the feller said that, because he appreciated how we'd gone out of our way to make him welcome, he'd give us a 'mates-rates discount' which, when he calculated it out, worked out to be fifty dollars a jar. So we borrowed some money off Ted, the publican, and we bought ourselves a jar each. Just a sample jar. Even Tugga.

'You'll never regret it,' the feller said and he told us that, when we run out of that lot, we could get in touch with him via the telephone number on the bottom of the label and he'd organise a shipment over for us right away at the same mates-rates discount.

So, to cut a long story short, we forked out a pretty hefty sum of money for these four tiny sample jars of this Johnson's Pawpaw Magic then we downed our beers and said 'Cheerio' to the bloke and we left the pub a fair bit earlier than usual.

Anyhow, next morning I gets this phone call from Blue. 'We've been diddled,' he said. 'The bloody stuff doesn't work. I've rung the other fellers. The same thing. We've been taken for a ride.'

'Oh yeah,' I said. 'Even Tugga?'

'Yeah,' said Blue, 'so we're goin' round to the pub to sort this feller out 'n' get our money back.'

'Oh, yeah,' I said.

'Are yer comin'?'

Now, here's the tricky bit. See, while it mightn't have worked for the other fellers, in my particular case, it did work. In fact, it was the best night that me and the wife had had for yonks. But what could I do, ay? I just couldn't tell me best mates that it'd worked fantastic for me. That'd only make them feel like they was duds, wouldn't it? Anyhow, best mates always stick together so I said to Blue, 'Yeah, the stuff was bloody crap. I'll be ready in ten. Pick me up on yer way through.'

But, as it turned out, when we arrived at the pub, the feller wasn't there. Ted told us that he'd left town earlier that morning on some sort of urgent business. So that was that. This bloke had got away with a couple of hundred quid and the ointment didn't work ... well, not on me mates, it didn't.

So that's basically the story and that happened about a year ago now and I've been trying to get in touch with the bloke, for him to send me over some more of the ointment. The only trouble is the telephone number that was wrote on the jar doesn't seem to work and I can't find hide nor hair of Johnson's Pawpaw Magic in the telephone directory. So things've been pretty desperate on the homefront and that's why I've rung you; you know, just on the off chance that, if he reads this story in a book, he'll get in touch with you and you can put him on to me. Thanks.

Swore Like a Trooper

(Railway Stories)

Then there was old Tommy Shortland. Christ almighty, he swore like a trooper, did old Tommy. He worked as a foreman in the parcels office at Spencer Street station when I was there, working for the railways. Like, when they delivered the parcels and that, it was Tommy's job to organise the sorting out of them and getting them on whichever train they were going on, north, west or whatever it was. Anyhow, old Tommy, it just come out of him without him even thinking about it.

I remember I was working in the receiving office one morning and an old lady came up to me and she was looking pretty upset. 'Who do I make a complaint to?' she asked.

I said, 'What do you want to make a complaint about?' 'Someone's swearing out the back there,' she said, 'and everyone in the railway station can hear it.'

Of course, I had a pretty fair idea who she was talking about, but to make it seem like I was going to get to the bottom of the matter, I went out into the parcels area and I called out, 'Hey, fellers, there's a woman here who wants to put in a complaint about someone swearing, so which one of youse was it?'

And Tommy stopped sorting out the parcels and yelled out to his fellow workers, 'Okay you mob'a bastards, quit the fuckin' swearin' or some old duck'll dob yer in the shit.'

Anyhow, I was extremely embarrassed about all this and I didn't know what I was going to say to the lady. But when I turned around she had a wry look on her dial. Like, she wasn't laughing about the swearing before, but after Tommy had called out what he'd just called out, she had a bit of a laugh at that. But I didn't know whether to laugh or not so I just apologised. 'Well,' I said, 'I'm very bloody sorry, love, but he just can't help his-self.'

Anyhow, she just laughed and went away. But you know, it sounded so funny because she was so serious at first. I mean, she could've reported him. But that's the way old Tommy was. He just didn't realise what was coming out of his mouth.

Now don't get me wrong, I'm not saying that Tommy wasn't a nice bloke or nothing, but in many ways he was a real bloody oddball. Yes, he was very loose with his language but, when it came to money, he was as tight as a fish's arsehole. Like, he used to love reading the *Sporting Globe*, I think it was — anyway, that sports newspaper. But he'd never buy one. So anybody who'd bought a *Sporting Globe* during the day, they'd leave it in the office for Tommy to read on his way home. Oh, he loved the *Globe*. It was funny; he didn't like any of the newspapers that had any news in them, he just loved the bloody *Globe*. That was his paper.

Anyhow, this Guido Leoni, a wog chap we also had working with us in the railways parcels office, he used to go home on the same train as Tommy and, one day, just as a joke, we doctored up Tommy's paper. See, we had the *Sporting Globe* and we got a copy of the *Catholic Weekly* and we took the racing section of the *Globe* out and we replaced it with the *Catholic Weekly*.

Then after work, Tommy grabs this newspaper and he goes and he settles himself on the train, ready to go home, and Guido settles right behind him, to gauge his reaction. So the train takes off and Tommy starts to read the bloody paper. Anyhow, after they'd gone a few stations, the carriage gets pretty packed with commuters. But Tommy doesn't notice because he's so engrossed with reading his beloved *Sporting Globe*. Then all of a sudden, he flips over the page and there's this bloody *Catholic Weekly*. Well, Guido told us that Tommy let go with such a spray of swearwords that there were train passengers taking off, out of there, in all directions.

'That'a carriage,' Guido said, 'she'a-vacuate real-a bloody quick.'

Stuck in the Shower

(Shearing Stories)

These days, if the shearers live within 50 or even 100 miles of a shed, the moment they knock off after a day's work they jump into their cars and drive home or to the nearest pub, where they'd more than likely be staying. But that didn't happen when I began shearing, forty years ago. I was around seventeen back then, and even when we were only 20 mile or so away from home we still camped out in the shearing quarters. And to my way of thinking that sort of lifestyle was far better because you got to know your workmates. You had more fun. There was more camaraderie, and that led to a few antics taking place.

And, with having just got out of the shower, there's a couple of bathhouse antics that spring immediately to mind. See, a lot of these shearing quarters weren't set up too well, especially when it came to bathing. Quite often they didn't have running water in the bath, so when that was the case you had to share the bathwater with the rest of the bloody blokes. Like, someone took first turn in the bath one night, then the next night someone else went first, and so on and so forth. You did it in rotation. That's what you did in them days.

But to keep the water warm over such a long time, you had to keep topping up the bath with hot water. Now, the hot water was usually boiled up in an old copper, and this copper could be situated anywhere. More often than not it was in the most inconvenient bloody place, like away around the back of the shed where you did your washing. So just before it was your turn to have a bath you had to go out to the copper and grab a couple of buckets of hot water.

Anyway, one time there were four of us camped out at a shed around the Nhill and Kaniva area, which is in the central-west of Victoria. The property was owned by the Allens. It was bath time and I was just about to get in when I remembered that I'd forgotten to go and get the hot water. So, with being out in the middle of nowhere, I didn't even bother about a towel or anything. I just zapped outside to grab a bucket of water out of the old copper. I was in the nick, like.

Now, what I didn't know was that Mr and Mrs Allen were out killing a sheep just a chain or so away. And neither did my mates know that they were there because, while I was outside getting the water, the bastards locked the door shut and I couldn't get back inside.

So there I was, as naked as the day I was born, a bloody bucket of hot water in one hand, banging on the door with the other, and calling out at the top of my voice, 'Let me back inside yer packa bastards.'

And I was just halfway through taking a deep breath so that I could let forth with another spray of profanities when this woman's voice come from just behind me. It was Mrs Allen.

'Are you alright, Terry?' she asked. Boy, did I shrink.

But, while we're on about shrinking, this one's definitely the opposite. Now, being locked out in the nick may have been one of my life's most embarrassing moments. But I can bloody well tell you there was an even worse one awaiting me. When I was in the same shed, this old guy set up a kind of shower affair. Now, why I say 'kind of shower' was because it was made up from, basically, one of those bloody old petrol driven pumps with a hand pump on it, which was fitted into a 44-gallon drum.

So if you wanted a shower, what you did, in effect, was that you stood in some water in the bath and cranked up the bloody hand pump until the petrol pump got going. And when she did, away she went, sucking the water through an inch and a quarter diameter hose, up out of the bath, and forcing it out of the shower head. Now it may sound complicated but it was quite effective because, once the petrol pump got going, by jeez, there was a hell of a strong pressure-flow coming out of the shower head.

Anyhow, one day I'm having a shower so I pumped the bloody hell out of this thing and I'd just got the petrol pump up to a full head of steam.

'Jeez,' I called out to Sandy, one of my shearing mates, 'you should came and have a look at this thing. It's a bloody powerful shower.'

Now, I must've been washing my hair or something because when Sandy came in I had my eyes closed. And this bastard, this Sandy, well, he pulled the suction end of the hose out of the bath. Now, he later swore black and blue that he didn't mean it and, if so, it was just a fluke shot but the next thing, 'Slap!' My donger gets sucked right up inside this bloody hose. Hell it was painful.

'Christ almighty,' Sandy said. 'Yer right. She's a powerful pump alright.'

And it was. I could vouch for that because there was my penis, stuck up the hose, good and proper. And what's more, the bloody thing wouldn't come out, no matter how hard I tried.

'Well, don't just stand there,' I threatened, 'bloody well do something.'

'What?' Sandy asked, scratching his head.

So he wandered off to get the other fellers to come in and see if they could sort the problem out. I tell you, there's not much bloody privacy in these shearing sheds, that's for sure. So there I was, stuck in the shower with my donger stuck up this length of hose and all these blokes gathered around, all smirking and shaking their heads from side to side and making all the wisecracks under the sun.

Anyway, after a lot of toing-and-froing one of the blokes said, 'Well,' he said, 'the only thing I can think of doing is to chop the bloody hose off to release the vacuum.'

So off he went in search of something to cut the hose. Now you might be able to imagine my reaction when this bloke returned, carrying a butcher's cleaver. Then to make me more nervous, the big discussion then began as to where they should sever the bloody hose, giving due consideration as to the amount of suck the pump had at the time of contact and the stretchability of the penis.

'And we don't wanta waste any of that hose neither,' some smart alec said. 'It's precious stuff, that plastic.'

Now, I'm not that well endowed but when they agreed to cut the hose just a few inches from the butt of my donger, my instant reaction was, 'Bullshit, yer will.' There was no way I was going to take any chances so I made bloody sure that the bastards cut the hose a good foot and a half from where it was stuck. And even then I was quaking at the knees as the cleaver came down.

Launceston, Tas

(Outback Towns and Pubs)

Now this story isn't about a little outback town or nothing but it's a little ripper about a pub in Launceston, Tasmania. The Apple Isle. Nice place, Launceston, lots of gardens and stuff. Pretty old. Don't know its history. Wouldn't have a clue. It's in the Tamar Valley, that's all I know, and I even stand corrected on that. I'm no historian. I'm a worker. An ex-shearer.

So it's the Commercial Hotel, Launceston. Early 60s. And this story's as true as I stand here, holding up the bar. See, the Commercial was one of the most popular pubs in Tassie because it was totally a union pub. Totally. If you were in the AWU, you were in. Not a worry. Even if you hadn't booked a room, it didn't matter. They got you in somehow. Then in the morning, if you could manage it, you fronted up to this huge kitchen-hall for breakfast and, boy, didn't you get a real good feed: bacon, eggs, sausages, chops, the lot. Whatever you wanted. But what the pub was really known for was their beautiful Sunday lunch. Just about everyone who had a union ticket would turn up for this feed, this Sunday lunch. Oh, they'd come for miles.

Okay, so we go into Launceston, a few workmates and me, and we go down to the Commercial. It's a huge, big, rambling hotel. Typically old style. Two-storey. We gets there on the dot of ten o'clock and the place's already packed. Absolutely packed. Lunch's about one. But, it doesn't matter, we show our ticket and we're in. Any rate, we have a few beers then we get stuck into this lunch. Absolutely beautiful. Everything you'd ever want and more. Then after lunch a mate and me decide to go for a bit of a poke around. Me mate's name's Ted. So we wander up to one of the rooms and, lo and behold, there's about twenty blokes playing poker, which, mind you, was a highly illegal activity. Any rate, I'm a bit buggered, right. A bit wobbly on the perch. So I just finds myself a spare bed and hits the sack. When I wake up I need some fresh air. 'I'm goin' fer a walk,' I say.

'I'll come with yer,' says Ted.

So that's what we do and somehow we end up down near Victoria Bridge. I don't know how we got there but we did. We hung around there for a while then we start thinking that we'd better go back to the Commercial and see what our workmates are up to. Now, by the letter of the law, pubs had to close up pretty early in Tassie, especially on a Sunday. So, by the time we get back, everything's sort of dead. The blinds are drawn and the place looks like it's closed down.

'Shit, what are we gonna do?'

Then we hears this racket coming from inside the pub.

'There's somethin' goin' on in there,' Ted says. 'Let's have a look.'

'Okay.' So we find the fire escape and we're up that. At the top of the fire escape there's this open window. In we go, straight into someone's room. 'Sorry, mate,' we say to the feller who's trying to get some kip. Through his room we go and down the old winding staircase, into the bar. And that's where everyone is. They're still drinking and carrying on.

So we settle back into the swing of things. After a while we see that the barman's falling off his perch. The barman's the owner. He's the publican. We give him a bit of a shake. 'How's about another beer?'

'Go fer it,' he says. 'I've had it.' Then he locked the till up, stuck the takings in the safe, and called out, 'Go fer yer lives, fellers. It's now an honour system.' Then off to bed he staggered.

Any rate, someone took over the bar and everybody just put their money down and that was that, we kicked on. Now, buggered if I know what time it was but, see, there's this bloke there with a big, red, woollen, fluffy sort of jumper on and he was starting to make a bit of a stir of things. A big, loud sort of feller he was. A real performer.

'Who's that?' I said to someone.

'Oh,' the feller said, 'he's the Birdman.'

And by geez he was a strange character. No exaggeration, this feller, the Birdman, he was at least twenty-four stone. Fair dinkum. Any rate, I just thought they called him the Birdman because of his fluffy jumper. But no, the feller next to me reckoned they called him the Birdman because, when he got good and pissed, he somehow got it into his head that he could fly.

'Pull the other one,' I said.

'Just you wait,' the feller said.

Any rate, just inside the entrance of the Commercial, there was this big, ornate staircase that winded up two tiers, to the residential part of the pub. So, Ted and me mate, we order a couple of jugs and we go and sit over with the rest of our mob. I'd say there would've been about a dozen of us at this wooden table. And it just happened that this table was right near the entrance, which also just happened to be under the landing of this staircase. So we're at this table and suddenly the Birdman calls out for everyone to shut up. Then, when all's quiet, he announces, 'I'm goin' fer a fly.'

Everyone gives him a bit of a cheer. 'Go fer it Birdman!' they started shouting. Apparently he was well known in Tassie and so they start a slow hand-clap to egg him on. So the Birdman got off his bar stool and he wobbled over to the staircase and proceeded to stagger up the two flights of stairs, right up to the top. Then, when the Birdman attempted to climb up on to the balustrade, high up, right up above our table, our boss grabs the remaining couple of jugs of beer from off our table and he calls out, 'Stand back, fellers!' Which we did, and pretty quick, too. So there's the Birdman, away up on this balustrade, two floors up. Everyone's slow-clapping him.

'I'm gonna fly,' he calls out. The clapping stops. There's dead silence. Everyone's eyes are on him. The Birdman balances himself on the balustrade. He fluffs up his big red jumper, gives a bit of a squawk, then he dives out into the air, arms spread wide like they're supposed to be wings. He manages a flap or two but it doesn't work. Down he comes, belly first, right smack-bang through the centre of our table. Splintered it.

Christ almighty, he didn't move a muscle. 'He's dead,' someone called out.

Then comes a ruffle of his woollen jumper. A shake of his head. He staggers to his feet. He's got this funny sort of grin on his dial. He looks straight at our boss, who's standing there, still hanging onto the two jugs of beer.

'What do yer reckon about that, then?' the Birdman slurred.

'Well, mate,' our boss replied, 'I must say that I was very impressed with the take-off but I reckon yer'd better brush up a bit on yer landings.'

Stiff

(Bush Funeral Stories)

Frank Partington here again. As you'd know I've been a contributor to a number of your books. Now, with regard to bush funerals and things, I did hear a story one time about a funeral director and his new female assistant. This reportedly happened in a town in the southern Riverina region of New South Wales, down near the Victorian border. Whether it's true or not is up for conjecture, so I'll tell it to you as it was more or less told to me.

The story goes that a funeral director was getting on a bit and he was looking forward to retiring from the industry within the next two or three years. The thing was, none of his family were keen on taking over the business. Now, as it happened, the best mate of the funeral director had a young daughter who was at a bit of a loss as to what to do with her life. I'd say she would've been just out of high school, so I'm guessing she might've been around sixteen, or eighteen at the most. So she was still quite young and quite naïve to adult life. Anyhow, the two fellers were having a chat about it in the pub one night and the funeral director offered to take on this young woman to see how she'd go. You know, as a sort of try-out apprenticeship type thing.

In due course the young female assistant arrived at the funeral director's for her first day's work. To make an impression upon her, the funeral director had gone the whole hog. This was back in the days when they wore top hats and tails and so forth, and he'd even gone to great lengths to sort out a complete set of funeral garb for her. So on her first morning, there they were, both of them dressed to the nines and the funeral director's taking the young woman through the basic procedure of what to do at a funeral service. As he was doing so, he noted how the young assistant seemed more intent on admiring herself in the mirror, dressed as she was in her new set of clothing, than she was on listening to him. Anyhow, the telephone rang.

'Could you please answer that?' asked the funeral director. 'I'm afraid that that's also going to be part of your duties.'

'Okay,' she said, and off she went. After she'd taken the call, the young woman came back to the funeral director. 'We've been asked to pick up a male stiff.'

The funeral director was then quick to explain that, within the industry, the newly departed were never to be called a 'stiff', but a 'cadaver' or 'deceased person'.

'Oh, okay,' she said, 'I'll try and remember.' Then she went back to admiring herself in the mirror.

'So,' the funeral director interrupted, 'did you take down the address?'

'Yes,' she said and she told him that it was 123 Whatever-the-name-of-the-street-was.

'Good,' he said. 'Well, let's go.' Then to impress the young woman even further, the funeral director decided to bend the rules a bit and, instead of taking his usual 'body removal vehicle' — an old Holden station wagon — he said, 'Let's take the hearse.'

So off they went. During the short drive to pick up this deceased male person, the funeral director explained to the young woman how the most important thing in situations like this is to maintain the utmost respectful silence for all those concerned. 'Oh, okay,' she said, 'I'll try and remember.'

When they arrived at the address, it was one of those duplex places which meant that there was a 123A and a 123B. The funeral director then asked the young woman, 'Do you remember if they said 123A or 123B?'

'It reckon it might've been 123A, I think, maybe,' she replied, not sounding too confident.

So the funeral director backed the hearse up into the drive of 123A ready for an efficient transfer of the deceased male person. When they got to the door, the funeral director gave a gentle knock. 'Is anybody home?' he announced himself in a soft tone.

At hearing no answer, he pushed the door slightly and, quite to his surprise he found that it was unlocked. 'Yes,' he said, now assured, 'this must be the right address.' Then he added, with a nod to his assistant, 'Remember to maintain a respectful silence at all times.'

'Okay,' whispered the young woman, 'I'll try and remember.'

So in they went. 'Hello? Hello? Is anyone at home?' the funeral director called in hushed ones. But no answer. Down the hallway, into the kitchen, a quick look out into the backyard but no; no one could be seen. So back into the house they came, with the young assistant following behind the funeral director. 'You check in the second bedroom. I'll check in the main one,' said the funeral director.

So they did. The funeral director went into the main bedroom while the young woman went into the second bedroom. And that's when the funeral director heard an audible muffled gasp. When he ran into the second bedroom, there was his new assistant, standing goggle-eyed, looking at the white sheet that was neatly covering the deceased male person. But it wasn't so much the discovery of the body that had shocked the young woman — bulging up from under the sheet was a huge erection. The funeral director was quick to put his finger to his lips as a sign for her to remain silent. Then he quietly explained that, if a man died while he had an erection, as the blood congealed, the erection would be held in its stiff position.

'I'll show you what we do,' whispered the funeral director, and he had a quick look around. At seeing the man's slippers beside the bed, he picked one of them up, cocked his arm back, and, to disperse the blood, he gave the undercover stiffened penis an almighty slap.

THWACK!

Like lightning a stark naked man leapt out from under the sheet. 'What the fucking hell are you two doing here?'

As the funeral director backpedalled into his ashen-faced female assistant, she whispered to him, 'Oops, perhaps I got my 123A's mixed up with my 123B's.'

Stan the Shearer

(Outback Police Stories)

I got this story from a bloke who knew a bloke who knew a bloke's missus who was the sister-in-law of the copper in question; a certain Sergeant Ignatius Kelly. It's a good old-fashioned Aussie yarn, told in the true tradition. So do you want to hear it?

Okay then, here goes. Back a good while ago now, Sergeant Kelly did a stint out at Broken Hill, in the far west of New South Wales. Anyhow, this Sergeant Kelly had apparently once told the story of Stan the shearer.

Stan the shearer apparently spent a lot of time working around the West Darling area. And after he got his pay cheque at the completion of each round of sheds, Stan would call his motley pack of dogs into the back of his old Chevy buckboard and he'd head for Broken Hill and, in particular, to his favourite pub, Brady's Southern. Now, as it happened, Brady's Southern was located in Patton Street, right across the road from the police station.

Just about everyone knew when Stan was arriving in town because, as soon as he turned off Bonanza Street and into Patton, they'd hear his old Chevy spluttering, muttering and clanging down the road with this pack of mangy mutts in the back, barking and yapping at everything that moved and most things that didn't.

'Shard-up, yer bloody mongrels,' Stan would be yelling. But the dogs never took any notice.

'Stan's back in town,' would be the common remark around the neighbourhood.

Then once Stan had come to a grinding halt at the pub, he'd step out of the buckboard, hunt the dogs into a wire compound at the back of the Southern, grab his bags, then walk through the back of the pub where he'd toss them into his usual room, the drunks' tank ... then he'd stride into the front bar.

'G'day,' he'd announce, like the returning prodigal, to which the regular three dowdy drinkers would wince and mutter, 'Shit, he's back.'

The only one who seemed anywhere near half excited about Stan's arrival was Bert, the publican, and that's because the next thing Stan would do was throw his shearing cheque down on the bar. 'Here, Bert,' he'd say, 'let me know when it's done,' and as Bert poured Stan the first of many more beers to come, he'd scoop up the cheque and stick it safely into his wallet. Actually I don't know how he'd do that; you know, pour a beer and stick a cheque in his wallet at the same time. He might've been ambidextrous or something. I don't know, but that's how I was told the story.

Anyhow, the thing is that while Bert was pouring Stan the beer and stashing the cheque away, he'd say, 'Now please, Stan, no trouble tonight, mate. Not like last time.'

'And the time before that,' would come the mutter from one of the three dowdy resident drinkers.

'And the time before that,' would sound another dowdy resident drinker.

'And the fuckin' time before that,' would chime in the third dowdy resident drinker.

'No worries, mate,' Stan would reply, wiping his wetted lips with his sheep-stained sleeve and shoving his empty glass forward for a refill, 'I promise ter be on me best behaviour. Honest,' to which the three dowdy resident drinkers would raise their eyes toward the pressed-tin ceiling of the pub, as if they'd heard all this a million times before. Which they had.

'I hope so, Stan,' Bert would say to no one in particular as he refilled Stan's glass.

Anyhow, this time around, as usual, Stan's promise came to nothing and later that night there's Stan, he's as full as a goog and rearing to have a stoush.

'Hey you,' he calls out to a burly miner known as Curly, 'do they call yer Curly 'cause yer so short?'

'Get stuffed, Stan,' retorts Curly at Stan's hint of his nickname deriving from short 'n curly.

'Get stuffed yerself,' slurs Stan.

'Here we go,' mutters the three dowdy resident drinkers in unison.

Anyhow, one thing then leads to another. Push leads to shove. Shove leads to shuffle, and then she's on. Stan and Curly are into it. Punches are thrown, left, right and almost centre, and the blue spills out of the front bar and onto the footpath.

By this stage, Sergeant Kelly's arrived on the scene. 'Righto, you two, that's enough. You, Curly, get home to yer missus 'n ten kids, 'n you, Stan, same as usual, you're coming with me,' and he pushes Stan in the direction of the police station.

'Thank Christ fer that,' mutter the three dowdy resident drinkers as they wander back into the pub to take up their well-worn bar stools.

'But, Sarge,' protests Stan, as he staggers across the road, 'how did yer know it was me what started the scrap?'

'Just a wild guess, I'd reckon, Stan; just a wild guess.'

Anyhow, early next morning Sergeant Kelly's at the cell door. 'Come on, Stan, wakey, wakey. Here's your usual: black tea with two sugars. The axe's in its normal place out beside the wood heap and I want the lot cut before you go and get those bloody dogs of yours and head out of town.'

Stan sits up, holding his head. His bloodshot eyes look like they've been run over by a grader. He has a couple of sips of tea, then he starts to pull on his boots.

'Look, Stan, how many times has this happened?' says Sergeant Kelly. 'Anyone'd think you'd have woke up to yerself after all these years, wouldn't they?'

'Yeah, yeah,' Stan replies as he shuffles outside to the wood heap. 'I guess I must be just one'a them slow learners, Sarge.'

'Well, this time, while you're back out in the shearing sheds, just have a good hard think about things, okay?'

'Yes, Sarge.'

Anyhow, a couple of months later the locals hear Stan's old Chevy coughing and spluttering down Patton Street, with his mob of mangy mutts barking at everything that moved and most things that didn't. Then as he passes the police station, Stan veers over to the wrong side of the road and, as he mounts the footpath, he nearly bowls over Sergeant Kelly. Amid the mayhem, Stan leans over into the back of his Chevy, grabs an axe and throws it over the back fence of the police station. Then he calls out, 'Sorry, Sarge. Almost gotcha,' before he continues on to his destination, Brady's Southern.

'That's it,' mutters the sergeant as he goes to grab his charge-sheet and head off to the pub.

As it happened, by the time Stan entered the front bar, Sergeant Kelly was already waiting for him; as were the three dowdy resident drinkers, full of expectation as to what excitement was about to unfold.

'What the bloody hell do you think you're doing, Stan, drivin' on the wrong side of the road, nearly bowlin' me over and throwin' an axe over my fence?'

'Well, Sarge,' Stan says, 'I've been thinking, like you said I should. See, you 'n me know exactly what's gonna happen, don't we? I'm gonna end up in me usual blue, right, 'n you're gonna drag me off ter the cell again, right, 'n the next morning yer gonna make me chop a pile of wood, right? So I thought this time I'd at least have a decent bloody axe.'

Resourceful

(Bush Funeral Stories)

To be involved in the funeral business, you must be a) very resourceful and b) due to the large number of back-to-back cremations we do these days, you also have to be extremely organised. So before the family and friends of the deceased arrive, the room in the crematorium, where the service is to be held, has to be all set up. I've got to have the order of service, and any of the personal words I'm about to deliver, double-checked by the family, printed out and ready to read. Any special songs or music the family may want played, or slideshow memories, have to be set to go at a press of a button. Out the back, the fire's already going, with the heat in the cremation chamber — the cremator — having been cranked up to about a thousand degrees.

The hearse then arrives. It pulls up out the front and the funeral directors take the casket, containing the body, into the cremation room, where it's put in place, down the front, on the plinth, or catafalque, which contains the mechanised insertion trolley. Any flowers, cards and well-wisher's paraphernalia are then placed on the casket, and we're set to roll.

I was doing a cremation one time. We'd done all the preparations; everything's in place. Then as everyone started to gather outside, one of the family members approached the funeral director. 'Look,' he said, 'do you mind if I just go in and pay my final respects to my mother before the service starts?'

The funeral director replied, 'Yeah, that's fine.'

Anyhow, this fellow went into the cremation room where the service was going to be held. A little kid tagged along behind him — his son I'm guessing. I'd say the boy would've only been about four or five. So they went in and I saw the bloke go over to the casket. And that's where the poor chap broke down. There must've been a lot of unresolved issues between the chap and his mother, which does often happen in families. Anyhow, this poor fellow, he just completely fell apart. He slumped over the casket and he started crying and sobbing and going on. Quite sad to see it was. So I let him be, allowing him some space to grieve, and I returned outside to mix with the family.

Now, you know what little kids are like. So there's the dad, all over the coffin, expressing his grief, and, as they do, this little kid soon gets bored. So he starts to wander around the place, having a look at this, a bit of a poke at that and somewhere along the line he must've spotted a red button.

What's this? he thinks.

So he pushes the red button. Next thing the insertion trolley kicks into gear and the casket starts to move from under the bloke. He doesn't know what to do. He's grappling; hanging on to the casket. Trying to pull it back. But it won't come back. He tries again. But no luck. So all he can do is to just stand there and watch as the casket, holding his mum, disappears behind the curtain. In a last grasp of hope he then decides to have a look behind the curtain, just in case there's any way he can stop it. But it's too late. The door of the cremation chamber opens, and the coffin disappears into a wall of flames.

Poof.

By this stage I'm still standing outside, mingling with the family. Next thing this bloke comes rushing out. He pulls me aside. He says, 'I ... I ... I don't know what happened. I was leaning on the coffin; next thing it started to move and now it's gone. The coffin's gone.'

I said, 'What do you mean the coffin's gone?'

He said, 'I ... I ... It's gone into the fire.'

Dear me. It was too late by now. His mum had just been inadvertently cremated.

But as chance would have it, another cremation service was due to start, straight after this one. So we whipped around the back to where the second hearse was waiting. As luck would have it, the casket was similar in style to the one that had just gone into the fire. Good; so we took it out of the hearse and we brought it in through the side door of the crematorium, out of sight, and we placed it on the plinth where the previous casket had been. After that was done, we took a moment to take a breath before we invited the bloke's family into the cremation room. And unbeknown to them, the whole service was conducted with a different deceased person laying in the casket.

When the service came to its end, we didn't send the casket off into the fire. We just closed the curtain in front of it. Then as soon as the family had departed, we took the unburnt coffin back around, put it in the waiting hearse and the hearse drove around the front, as if nothing untoward had happened.

Like I said, you have to be resourceful.

Kingoonya, SA

(Outback Towns and Pubs)

Well Kingoonya, in South Australia, was always just a rail maintenance town and that's all. It came into being during the construction of the Trans-Australian Railway Line, across the Nullarbor. And something that's quite unique about it is that the pub — and I've only ever known it as the Kingoonya Hotel — was owned by the same family, the Brett family, right from the day it was built, in 1914, right through till it shut down, which was in about the late 1980s, I'd say. But, in my time, in about 1982–83, other than the hotel, Kingoonya only had a bakery and a little shop and, to the best of my knowledge, the population never got above fifty.

But then, see, when the concrete sleepers were inserted into the Trans-line and the rails were 'continuously welded', the track required much less maintenance and so the Railways closed down a lot of those small places across the Nullarbor, like Tarcoola and Rawlinna and the rest of them. But, even then, the township of Kingoonya somehow managed to struggle on for a bit till it eventually withered away, like a slow death, and they finally had to close the pub. Though, the good news is that, with the better roads and better transport these days, a lot of the buses go out to Kingoonya before they turn off and go south, down to the west coast of South Australia. And they tell me that the little pub, she's up and running once more, though I don't think the Brett family are involved in it.

Anyway, my story is back when I was working through the area, a good friend of mine was working at Kingoonya, a bloke called Terry Sharpe. Terry was the Road Foreman, in charge of a group of about sixty men, inserting something like 1500 of these cement sleepers per kilometre of the rail line. Anyhow, I was the Superintendent-in-Charge of the continuous-welded-rail across the Trans-line and, Terry and me, we had our camps adjacent to one another. Now, Terry was a former policeman and military man, and I don't know whether you know any military people or not but, usually, you can tell them a mile off because that's all they talk about — the military. Still, he was a bloody hell of a good bloke and a real bloody wag.

So, this day, I was in the camp and the next minute a bloke comes running across to me and he's pretty anxious and he said, 'Yer'd better go 'n' see Sharpie, he's been shot.'

'Oh, Jesus no.' Anyway, I went and saw Terry and here he was, in his room, laying on the bed. So I said to him, 'What the hell happened to you?'

He said, 'I've just been shot.'

'Oh yeah, how?'

'Well,' he said, 'I was over at the pub and there was some sorta argument with a bloke about a bloody dog 'n' the bloke walked away 'n' he came back with a .22 calibre rifle. So I thought I'd better take it off him. You know, disarm him. So that's what I was attempting to do when he shot me.'

'Jesus,' I said, 'where did yer get shot?'

At that, Terry looked a bit embarrassed, then he mumbled, 'In the backside.'

Now, like I said, because Terry's ex-military, he's forever talking about his service days and what he did do and what he didn't do and what he should've done and what he would've done and whatever. Very proud of his time in the military. I said to him, 'Well, thank Christ there's not a war on.'

He said, 'Why's that?'

I said, 'Because you'd be labelled a bloody coward.'

Now, being ex-military and being a coward is about as low as you can get. So now he's pretty agitated. He says, 'And what the bloody hell do yer mean about me being labelled a coward?'

I said, 'Well, if yer got shot in the arse then, obviously, yer must'a been runnin' away.'

Anyway, he wasn't too pleased about that. But, the long and the short of it was that, being ex-military, his pride was bruised and so he refused to go and see anyone about it.

So he's still got this bullet in his bum and he's staggering around the place, like a bear with a sore head, and so his blokes are coming to me and they're saying, 'Look, Ted, you'd better go 'n' talk to Terry, he's getting crankier by the minute.'

So in the end I went and seen him and I said, 'Fer Christ's sake, Terry,' I said, 'come on, I'll take you into Woomera.' Woomera being the nearest hospital. I said, 'We'd better get this bullet taken out 'n' get you fixed up.'

But, no, he still wasn't too keen on it. Perhaps my remark about being called a coward had got to him and he was out to prove some point or other. I don't know. He said, 'I tell yer, Ted, there's no way I'm gonna go all the way ter Woomera just ter have some inexperienced nurse dig a piddly little bullet outa me bum.'

So I said, 'Terry, you know what's gonna happen, don't you?'

'No. What?'

'Well, if we don't get that bullet taken out, mate, your epitaph's gonna read something like you see in the American old west, up on Boot Hill somewhere.'

'What do yer mean by that?' he said.

'Well,' I said, 'your headstone's gonna read "Died of friggin' lead poisoning after being shot in the bum". Now, mate,' I said, 'is that the image yer want'a leave about your life?'

Anyway, that convinced him. 'Yeah, okay,' he says and so I took him into the hospital at Woomera and they cut this bullet out of him. So that was it. He survived and now lives in Launceston, in Tasmania, and if you ever get in touch with him and ask him about his days in Kingoonya, I reckon he'll say something along the lines of it being 'a pain in the friggin' arse'.

I'm the Minister

(Bush Priests Stories)

I'll just finish off with this one, shall I? It's a funny little story. See, my ministry used to take in a lot of the north of South Australia, so every now and then I'd go out and stay a few days at a little opal mining place called Mintabie. To give you some idea, Mintabie's just a couple of hundred kilometres south of the Northern Territory border and, even though it's in the APY Lands — the Anangu Pitjantjatjara Yankunytjatjara Lands — the township has a mainly non-Indigenous population. I'd say there'd only be a hundred or so people living there and there's a pub and a small school.

When I'd go to Mintabie I used to stay at the pub and, gee, we had some great times. Never failed. But while I was in Mintabie I'd go over to the school each day and have morning tea with the teachers and that. So this particular day I was in the staffroom having a cuppa when I heard the female receptionist say to someone in the foyer, 'No, you're not the minister. The minister's already here. He's out the back having morning tea with everyone.'

Then a woman replied in this lovely English voice, 'But he can't be. I am the Minister.'

'No you're not,' the receptionist said. 'The minister's out the back. We had a drink with him last night in the pub and he's here today and he's going to do a service later on.'

'My dear friend,' the woman said, 'believe you me, I am the Minister.'

'No you're not.'

'Yes I am.'

Anyhow, just from the woman's voice, I knew who it was. So I got up and I went out into the foyer and I said, 'Hello, Jane.'

'Hello, Reverend John,' she said. 'Good to see you again.'

I said to the receptionist, 'Oh, I'd like to introduce you to Jane Lomax-Smith, the Minister for Education.'

'Oh,' she replied. 'Sorry. I didn't realise.'

'Don't worry,' I said. 'It happens to me all the time.'

Jane and I had a great laugh about that. She loves telling that story too.

Where's the Barra?

(Railway Stories)

My name's Brian Gibbs and between 1956 and 1961 I was the officer-in-charge of the Normanton to Croydon Railway, in the north-west of Queensland. That particular piece of track is reputed to be the most remote and isolated rail line in Australia. Anyhow, I drove the petrol-driven rail motor, more commonly known as a Tin Hair, on its weekly trip from Normanton to Croydon and return, and I'd like to share a couple of short memories of my time with that grand old rail motor, officially named the 'Gulflander'.

Back in 1956 we had a huge cyclone in the Gulf of Carpentaria, the results of which caused widespread damage and many rivers to flood. From memory, two people lost their lives in Georgetown. That's how bad it was. Anyhow, as the cyclone continued its journey over towards Cairns we were still keen to do our weekly trip, which we did, and the rail motor made it to Croydon okay.

But when we started back to Normanton on the Thursday morning, we only got 20 miles and we found that the Seventy-Four Mile Creek bridge was covered with floodwater. She was well over the top. Anyhow, I decided that we should still have a go at crossing the bridge, but then the flywheel became covered with water and it consequently splashed water all over the engine. That was no good, so we were forced to reverse the Gulflander all the way back to Croydon. The best we could do on the return was 5 miles an hour, which made it a very long journey.

The following morning, the Friday, we detached two wagons and we set out once again for Normanton, hoping now that the creek was crossable. But when we came to the Seventy-Four Mile creek, the level of the water was much the same. So this time we shut the motor off and decided that our best option was to push the vehicle through the water, over the bridge, which proved to be a considerable distance. After much effort we made it, though I felt that we were lucky because the railway line was flat and did not dip, as it did at other points along the way. Mind you, in saying that, as we continued the journey we were forced to get out and push the rail motor at three more locations. When we eventually reached the Norman River, the water was a good four to six inches above the rails and, with a little care plus a good slice of luck, we were just able to cross the river and head towards our destination of Normanton. And we made it, but due to the severe flooding that soon followed we were unable to continue the rail motor service to Croydon for the next ten weeks.

So that's one memory. Another one's how the patrons in at the pub in Croydon often used to complain that they'd never seen any of the barramundi — or barra, as we call it — I'd apparently skited so much about catching in the Norman River, at Normanton.

'Okay then,' I said, 'I'll prove it to you.' 'Yeah,' they replied. 'When?'

'Next trip,' I said.

With that settled, the following Tuesday afternoon, John Hindmarsh, the then Powerhouse Superintendent, and myself went fishing at Glenore, about 12 miles south-east of Normanton. I was very confident of a good catch there because I knew a nice little spot beside the rail bridge, over the Norman River.

Anyhow, we fished out of a rowing boat, trailing a lure, and before long we'd caught two nice sized barra, one about 15 pounds, the other around 18 pounds. Seeing how my next trip to Croydon was just the following morning, I decided that I'd really give the blokes at the pub a treat and I'd deliver these two fish to them nice and fresh. With that in mind, John and I proceeded to tie a line to the mouth of each of the fish. We then placed them in a large waterhole, in the river, under the bridge. Finally, we tied the other end of the lines to a tree, then we left the barra there to swim and stay alive. The next morning it was just a simple matter of stopping the rail motor on the bridge, going down, collecting the fish and taking them to Croydon where I'd prove to all my doubters, once and for all, just what a great fisherman I was.

So on the Wednesday morning I stopped the Gulflander on the bridge and hurried down to the waterhole. I pulled on one of the lines, but no fish. The line was broken. I had a look around and I saw the barra up on dry land, about 4 yards away. 'This's funny,' I thought. 'The only way it could've got up that far was if it'd been thrown or it'd somehow jumped out of the waterhole.'

When I tried the other line it seemed to be snagged, so I gave it a good pull. But no, it was stuck firm. By this stage the passengers in the rail motor were looking expectantly down at me so I thought, 'Geez, I'd better not disappoint them.'

So I removed one shoe and the sock and I stuck my foot in the waterhole and manoeuvred it around in an attempt to clear the snag. No, that didn't work. It was hooked on something solid; something that felt very much like a rough log. 'Blow it,' I thought, so I grabbed the line again and gave it one hell of a yank and up shot the head of a crocodile, jaws open and ready for a fight.

Well, bugger the fish — they could say what they darn well liked in at the Croydon pub. I was out of there in a shot, much to the amusement of my rail passengers.

Tibooburra, NSW

(Outback Towns and Pubs)

I've got a story here from up the far north-west of New South Wales, at a place called Tibooburra. It was told to me by a mate of mine, R. Paul Brady, and it comes from a book he wrote called *Silver, Lead and Saltbush*. It's a good read too, if you can get hold of a copy.

Now the name of Tibooburra comes from the Aboriginal word for 'heaps of rocks', which might give you some idea what the first white fellers came across; fellers like Charles Sturt who passed by in the mid-1840s, looking for the inland sea, then Burke and Wills, fifteen or so years later. So there wasn't too much to enthuse anyone until gold was discovered in the late 1880s. Of course, with the whiff of gold in the air, thousands of hopefuls soon arrived and so the town grew out of that.

But, when the gold days passed, the place lost its appeal, what with nine out of ten years being in drought, stinking hot summers, freezing cold winters and the winds, both summer and winter, so bad that you had to make sure the dunny door was shut or you'd lose it. Even into the 50s, when this story took place, Tibooburra still didn't have electricity or gas. So you had to be made of pretty stern stuff to live out there, which most people aren't and so, if you would've fired a shotgun down the main street, the chances of hitting someone would've been next to none.

Anyhow, there was this bloke in Tibooburra, see. A small, fat bloke. A bootmaker by trade. From Greece he was. His name was Peter Christapoulas or just Pete to his mates though, mind you, he didn't have too many mates because whenever he got a bit of coin he'd be off to the pub, where he'd get on the turps and try to pick a fight. Pete lived out on the Dead Horse Creek side of town in an old lean-to made from rusted corrugated iron and flattened old kerosene tins. Of course, being made from corrugated iron and kerosene tins, he was more or less open to the elements; like, if it was hot, he sweltered, if it was cold he froze. So that's where Pete lived and he lived on the smell of an oily rag, with just a mattress on the dirt floor, a bit of a stove, cupboards made out of fruit boxes.

But there was one event held in Tibooburra that attracted people from all over. It was the annual weekend race meeting, and even though it was on when the first chill of winter blew in, they'd still come from everywhere — Broken Hill, Menindee, Wilcannia; some even from as far as Quilpie and Thargomindah. And so, when this race meeting was on, all the station owners, ringers, shearers, bookies, bludgers and what-have-you, who came to town, took the opportunity to get their boots mended. So Pete'd be flat out with his tack hammer, raking in the dough.

Now there were two watering holes still standing from the olden days; one was Barney's Pub and the other was Tibooburra Hotel and so, after the race meeting was over, Pete'd be cashed up and he'd go on a binge. First port of call was Barney's but, after he'd had a few, sure enough, he'd try to pick a fight with some poor unsuspecting bugger and it wouldn't be long before Barney'd boot Pete out of his pub. 'Bugger off, Pete,' he'd say and out Pete'd stagger, out of Barney's, abusing everyone in Greek and he'd stumble over to Tibooburra Hotel, where he'd have a few more and try to pick a fight there. Loved a stoush he did. So it'd be, 'Bugger off, Pete,' and Pete'd stagger out of the Tibooburra, into the biting wind, and stumble home to his corrugated iron and flattened kerosene lean-to. That was his pattern after race weekend, night after night, till all the money was gone.

Anyhow, just after this particular race weekend, the local copper, Sergeant Bill Holmes, checked his wood heap and seeing that it was getting low he got in touch with the local odd-job bloke and organised a load. The only trouble was that, when the wood arrived, it arrived in an uncut state. Worse still, it was a mix of gidgee and mulga which, as you might know, are about the hardest woods to cut. Now, Sergeant Holmes had an aversion to physical activity so it was, 'Bugger it'. Then, just as he was thinking that he'd have to chop the lot himself, he heard a ruckus over at the Tibooburra Hotel. 'Here's a go,' he said and he strode over to the pub.

Of course, it's Pete, pissed as usual and throwing a few at some stockman or other who'd drifted in from Naryilco.

'What the bloody hell's goin' on here?' says the Sarg.

Pete says, 'This bastard won't pay me fer fixin' his boots.'

'Friggin' well did, Sarg,' says the stockman, 'but he's too pissed ter rememb'a.'

'Okay,' says Sergeant Holmes, 'I'll sort this out.' So the Sarg said to Pete, 'Pete, piss off home 'n' meet me at the station tomorra mornin'. I've got a little job fer yer.'

Nobody argued with Sergeant Holmes. Nobody. Not even Pete. And so it was, 'Okay, Sarg,' and Pete staggered out into another freezing night and headed back to his corrugated iron and kerosene tin lean-to.

Then the Sarg said to the stockman, ''N' you bugger off tomorra as well.'

'Okay,' said the stockman, and he staggered out the back, crawled into his swag and he pissed off at first light, swearing that he'd never come back to Tibooburra — for two reasons: Pete and the bitter cold.

Anyhow, next morning, there's Pete. He's at the police station. There'd been a black frost. He's shivering. The Sarg gives him an axe and a wheelbarrow and points him to the pile of wood. 'There yer go, Pete, chop that lot 'n' stack it nice 'n' neat over b' the house. It'll soon warm yer up.'

'But, Sarg?'

'No buts about it, 'n' I want it all done b' the time I get back from me rounds.' His rounds took in places like White Cliffs, Wanaaring and Milparinka. That's most of the day.

'Yeah, okay, Sarg.'

So the Sarg jumped in his truck and off he went and Pete gets stuck into the wood.

Anyhow, it was a long day. As I said, you'd hardly get tougher timber than gidgee and mulga. But when the Sarg returned from his rounds, that evening, there was Pete finishing off the last of the wood and stacking it in a neat pile over by the house. The Sarg, he inspects the woodheap. 'Geez,' he says, 'I thought there would'a been more wood than that?'

'Well,' says Pete, 'what yer've gotta realise, Sarg, is that I cut it up so neat 'n' I packed it in so tight that it looks like there's less than what there is.'

'Yeah, suppose so,' says the Sarg. 'Well, off yer go 'n' fer Christ's sake, Pete, go easy on the piss or yer'll be back ter do another load.'

'Yes, Sarg,' says Pete, and off he went back home. Then when he got there, he knocked the top off a beer, dragged a chair over near the stove, put his feet up onto a nice pile of freshly cut gidgee and mulga and said, 'Here's ter you, Sarg.'

Aladdin's Lamp

(Railway Stories)

Railways run in the Nicholls family. My grandfather was a train driver at Kalgoorlie. It might sound a bit odd, but even though he was stationed in Western Australia he was employed by SAR (South Australian Railways). Then my father was a cook with the Commonwealth Railways; my uncle was a fireman with them as well. But I was a cleaner at Oodnadatta first, then one day the fireman on the Ghan took crook so they grabbed me to do the firing back to Quorn, and that's how I became a fireman. Then I went on to be a driver.

In those days the old Ghan line went from Port Augusta through Quorn, Hawker, Copley, Marree, Coward Springs, William Creek, Oodnadatta, Eringa, then up into the Northern Territory through Fink, Ewaninga and on to Alice Springs. See, a lot of people have the idea that only one Ghan train worked the line but there were heaps of others. Other than the passenger train there were stock trains, goods trains — you name it — work trains, coal trains, the lot. Now as far as dates go, let me think; I left the Commonwealth Railways not long after I got married in 1950. Yes, that's right, because I met my wife, Coral Brooks, in Quorn, in '48. So I joined SAR in 1951, then I became a fireman, then a driver in 1953, and then that became AN (Australian National). But to be a driver on the Ghan in the old days was a real bloody honour, you know, because it was only the senior men, like the firemen, the guards and drivers, that ever worked the line.

But there were some characters, I can tell you. We had one guard by the name of Pud and, gawd, he'd pinch the milk out of your bloody coffee. You can't mention this, of course, but when we were working the cattle trains, if any of the cows calved along the way, to save them being trodden on and die, Pud'd take them down to the compo-brake van and put them in the bloody shower recess.

The shower recess was the only place you could keep them, otherwise they'd shit everywhere. So there they'd be, all these bloody newborn calves in the brake van going, 'Moo, moo, moo', all bloody night.

Then when we got home, Pud'd take all these calves out to his place and, over time, he ended up with this bloody great big herd of cows. Oh, he had Herefords, he had Black Polls. He had bloody everything, which, of course, he then sold at a 100 per cent profit. Then there's another story about Pud, which I also shouldn't mention. It was during the war and he was on a supply train going to the Alice and there was all this timber on a flat top. Well, Pud's got his eye on this timber, see, because he knows that he's got a few jobs back home that it could be used for. Anyhow, Pud knows that there's going to be a change of crew at Peak Creek; just before you get to Algebuckina. So the train stops there in the middle of the bloody night in amongst all these sandhills and Pud's up on the bloody flat-top sliding along this timber with the aim of hiding it in the sandhills and picking it up on his return journey. Anyhow, he's moving all this timber about and a bloody torchlight hits his eyes.

It was the provos, the military police.

'What do you think you're doing?' one of the provos said. 'Thank Christ yer came along,' Pud replied. 'Some'a the bloody timber's coming off and I need a hand to get it back up on the flat-top.'

I mean, how's that for presence of mind, eh? But that was Pud. He was a nice guy but, as I said, give him half a chance and he'd nick the milk out of your coffee.

Then there's another favourite story of mine about a different bloke, a bloke called Bonny Fry. Bonny was the train examiner in Alice Springs. Geez, wasn't he a rough diamond. As a train examiner, it was Bonny's job to go along and check the brakes and everything on the Ghan before it departed the Alice. Now, I'd just finished shunting and I was going back to rest-out and, on that particular Monday, the Ghan was late leaving. Anyhow, I hooked up with Bonny and we were having a chat while he was doing this testing, and we came across this sleeping car.

Well, back in those days they had, like, the long-drop toilets on the trains. There wasn't even a pan or anything, so your business just went straight down onto the track. Inside the carriages they had all these signs telling everybody not to use the toilets while the train was standing at the station. Anyway, Bonny and me were going along beside this sleeping car and we hear this 'plop, plop' on the ground, and we see this stuff coming out the bloody chute.

'Gawd,' said Bonny, 'I've gotta clean this bloody mess up after they go.'

Now, Bonny had what was called a slush light. If you can imagine, a slush light's an oil can with a bloody big wick on it. To give you some idea, it's shaped exactly like a huge Aladdin's lamp. It was a hell of a size. Anyhow, he lights this Aladdin's lamp-looking thing, and he shoves it straight up the flue. Next thing, the window flies open but, instead of a beautiful genie appearing to grant us three wishes, this old dowager sticks her head out and, boy, didn't she start abusing poor old Bonny. Gawd, she was as mad as hell.

'Well, lady,' he said, 'if yer wanta have a shit here, then have it in the bloody station toilets where you're supposed to have it.'

But, geez, that lamp had a hell of a flame on it. I reckon it must've burnt every hair on her bum, and more besides.

Pauper's Funeral

(Bush Funeral Stories)

Now, no doubt you've heard different versions of this story before but, as true as I stand here, this version is the absolute fair-dinkum, ridgy-didge one. It was told to me by a mate of mine called Wally. Wally was born and bred in Humpty Doo, which is where the original incident occurred. For those that may not know, Humpty Doo's just off the Arnhem Highway, about twenty or so miles south of Darwin. These days it's got a population of near on five thousand, and the first thing that strikes you when you roll into town is the statue of the Boxing Crocodile. You can't miss it. It's thirty feet high; maybe more. But this was long before the Boxing Crocodile was even thought of. It happened just at the beginning of the people-shift down to Humpty Doo, where the blocks of land were larger and yet still within easy commuting distance from the hustle and bustle of Darwin.

Okay, so there was this Scottish feller. You could describe him as being pretty much a loner type. He lived in spare conditions; nothing more than a tin shed, on the very outskirts of Humpty Doo. So it was right out in the bush and, like many Territorians, he was a bit of a drinker. He liked his grog. Wally told me that a couple of mates of his used to have a few with the Scottish feller whenever he came into town.

Anyway, Wally's mates hadn't seen the feller for a while and so they went out to see if he was okay. When they stumbled into the feller's shed, there he was, stinking to high heaven, sitting bolt upright in his armchair, with a can of beer in his hand and his glassy eyes staring blankly at a fervently flickering television set.

'Shit,' they said, 'he's as dead as a doornail.' A heart attack or some such, the doctor later reckoned.

The thing was, when the powers that be looked into the Scottish feller's background, he didn't seem to have any family in Australia. What's more, he was skint, as broke as a badger. So with little to no means to his name the local authorities decided that he'd be given what's called a pauper's funeral. As I said, this all happened at a time when Humpty Doo was just starting to expand and so there was a lot of infrastructure work going on; you know, stuff like the kerbing and guttering of the new streets, sewerage and stormwater systems being laid. Even the cemetery was getting a new office, a small chapel for services, along with toilets and so forth for the convenience of the mourners.

Now, when it came to organising the funeral for this pauper, the local priest thought that, at the very least, the poor feller should be given a send-off themed as close to his homeland as possible. To that end he got in touch with a mate of his, Brian, who was the lead bagpiper in Darwin's Scottish Highland Pipe Band. After explaining the situation, the priest asked Brian if he'd like to pop down to Humpty Doo on the day of the funeral and farewell the feller by playing a couple of Scottish tunes.

'Yep,' said Brian, 'it's the least I can do for the poor bugger.'

So all was organised. The service was to be held at the gravesite and there'd only be Brian and the priest, plus Wally's mates from the pub who'd found the feller. Oh, and seeing how it was smack-bang in the middle of the wet season, a couple of gravediggers would be there, at the ready, to fill in the hole before the next deluge hit and, as well as having died from a heart attack or some such, the poor Scottish feller would also be drowned.

As it happened, the day of the funeral was a howler. It's raining cats and dogs and, to make matters worse, Brian's car refuses to start. It was something to do with the electrics and so he had to call the AANT — Automobile Association of the

Northern Territory. By the time they got him up and going, he's running over an hour late. Anyway, Brian tosses the bagpipes in his car and he high-tails it down to Humpty Doo. By the time he gets there, it's stopped raining. He rushes around to the Humpty Doo Cemetery but there's no one there. The funeral's over. The priest's packed up and gone home and Wally's mates have returned to the pub to continue their commiserations.

Of course, Brian's feeling pretty wretched about the pauper having been buried without a decent Scottish send-off. 'Shit,' he says, 'what can I do?'

Then he sees a couple of gravediggers filling in the hole over the far side, near the new chapel and administration block. 'That's it,' he says and he grabs his bagpipes and he heads off to the gravesite. So eager is he to make up for lost time that, even before he reaches the site, he's pumped up his bagpipe and he's into full swing with Rabbie Burns' 'My Love is Like a Red, Red Rose'. Midway across the cemetery he realises that 'My Love is Like a Red, Red Rose' mightn't be the most suitable of funeral tunes, so he then changes tact and breaks into another Rabbie Burns favourite, 'Ye Banks and Braes of Bonnie Doon'. By the time he gets to the grave, the two gravediggers have stopped filling in the hole and they're standing there to greet him with their shovels respectfully held by their sides.

Without a breath, Brian then burst into another Scottish favourite, 'Amazing Grace'. The thing was, halfway through the first verse, Brian started to think about his own life's situation. It'd been a difficult couple of months. Due to his excess drinking and a few of his other bad habits, his wife had left him and she'd taken off down south with their two teenage daughters. So then, in his own way, Brian started think about the similarities between himself and the Scottish pauper. He could imagine the situation where, if he got sick, there'd be no one there to care for him. Worse still, if he died at home, he could well go like the pauper — as dead as a doornail, sitting upright in his armchair, with a can of beer in his hand and his glassy eyes staring blankly at a fervently flickering television set.

And the more Brian thought about the situation, the more emotional he became, and, the more emotional he became, the more emotional did his playing become. By the third verse, Brian had got it in his head that this could well be his own funeral: a pauper's funeral with a lone piper like himself playing 'Amazing Grace' and with just two other blokes — gravediggers — in attendance. And that's when the tears began to flow. Then as he reached the final refrain of 'Amazing Grace', he looked across and there were the two gravediggers also shedding a tear or three.

When he'd finished playing, a solemn silence fell as Brian and the gravediggers stared down into that three-quarter-filled hole.

'I must apologise,' Brian said to the two men, 'this's the first time I've played at a pauper's funeral, and I'm a bit emotional.'

'Well,' said one of the diggers, sniffling back the tears, 'it's the first time we've ever had a piper play at one of our septic tank installations.'